Folkore and Legends of Trinidad and Tobago

Folklore and Legends

of

Trinidad and Tobago

written and collected by Gérard Besson

Design and Layout by Gérard and Alice Besson
Original Illustrations by Alfred Codallo, Avril Turner, Peter Shim, Stuart Hahn
and Sue Anne Gomes
Pre-Press and Printing by Caribbean Paper and Printed Products (1993) Limited
60A Boundary Road, San Juan, Trinidad, W.I.

Fourth edition 2008

ISBN: 976-8054-47-6

Contents

Dedication

To my grandchildren

Daniel and Hannah.

Since me born
Me nebber de know
Crapaud is wear shirt and pants.

Since me born
Me nebber de know
Crapaud is going to dance.

Preface

LONG AGO, AS CHILDREN, we would often go to the country for the long summer vacation. One of the distinct memories surviving from those times, along with those of river and sea excursions, huge meals and friends made for life, is of the stories that were told.

Sometimes my father or Uncle Hecky would tell jumbie stories in the darkening twilight as the kerosene lamps with their "Home Sweet Home" chimneys threw out huge, wavering shadows onto the walls. We all crowded round to listen to his hair-raising, heart-thumping tales of terrible creatures and terrifying accounts of encounters with the supernatural.

More often than not they were created on the spot, as my Aunt Polly's smile would reveal, as she looked at my father with mild surprise when some incredible variant of an old tale came into his head. Drawing from a vast stock of standard information on the various characters, he was able to innovate and create narratives that could cause us to either laugh with relief or quake in our shoes. This book seeks to show what these creatures look like and to tell something of their various attributes.

We have drawn some fragments form Harry Pitts' *The Folklore of Trinidad*, an unpublished manuscript now lost, which was contributed to by famous folklorists Alfred Codallo and Charles Adrian Espinet. We have also used *Legends of the Bocas*, published in 1922 by Alexander David Russell; *Ti-Jean and his Brothers* by Derek Walcott, published by Paria Publishing; *Mermaids and Fairy Maids or Water Gods and Goddesses of Tobago* by H.B. Meikle, published by Caribbean Quarterly in 1957; papers on the subject by Ari Boomert and Dr. Phillip Sherlock of the University of the West Indies; Shelley Marshall's thesis *Ties that bind - the Mama Glo tradition in the French Caribbean and in Trinidad and Tobago;* and *Folklore and Legends* and *Tales of the Paria Main Road*, collected by myself and published by Paria. Andrew Pearse's collections of stories of *Mitto Sampson*, published in Caribbean Quarterly in 1957, was as valuable a source as was Fr. Anthony de Verteuil's *Scientific Sorties* and Carton Ottley's little book about Tobago. Two stories were taken from Hersketh Bell's book *Obeah— Witchcraft in the West Indies*, published first in 1889, which shows that our folklore was already of interest to an international audience more than a century ago.

A most valuable source of oral traditions was Anita Tardier, who in her old age shared the folklore of the Paramin mountains with me. Olga Mavrogordato was my mentor and the original source not only for Trinidad's folklore but also for a great love of Trinidad and Tobago's history.

The illustrations are mainly done by Stuart Hahn, Avril Turner, Peter Shim, Sue Anne Gomes and Alfred Codallo. We thank Angostura Limited and Hand Arnold Limited for permission to reproduce Alfred Codallo's series of folk illustrations.

We also would like to express our gratitude to Derek Walcott for permission to use the excerpt from his wonderful book *Ti-Jean and his Brothers*.

Thanks to Rhett Gordon of Caribbean Paper & Printed Products Limited for immediately endorsing this project, and to Jonathan Costelloe for assisting with the production.

Finally, I would like to thank my wife Alice for her kind help and encouragement in making this book possible.

The reader should familiarise himself with the material presented; he should make free his imagination; and, perhaps with the aid of a little rum, a dark night, a good audience and the right soundtrack of croaking frogs and hooting owls, he should seek to entertain his young charges with tales and stories from the ancient childhood of our past. Every story should end with the words:

Crick Crack
Monkey break he back
For a piece of pomerac.

or: *Crick Crack the wire bends,*
And that's the way my story ends.

In that way you would be sure that any spirit who may have crept into your midst would be banished away for good.

Gerard Besson
Carnival Monday, February 2001

Papa Bois

THIS IS THE STORY OF the Ancient One who lived in the heights; who, walking through the forest, never met his like. At that same time, morning broke, bright gold—and the moon, unable to get away, stayed to look, together with a little bit of night towards the western edge of the world. The child cried as his mother's labour was done. She, through her tears, could see two great globes on either side of the sky: the sun, in gold to the east, rising, and the moon, in silver, waning to the west.

"A traveller," said the old woman. "He will walk across the world."

The seasons came and went. The boy grew without name. In good time, they felled a giant tree, and, with tools of stone, made a great corial, and set out for the Land of the Humming Bird, which they called Iere. Waves, like giant green horses, beat the air. Foam flicking in their hair, the men in the long canoe shot their craft like an arrow through the waves, towards the beach carved in white out of the green hillsides, ever rising into mammoth shapes beneath a blanket of deep green.

He looked around and saw that he was alone in the plunging sea. Boat, old woman, men, mother, bags of yam, a lappe, all gone. Great breakers tossed him onto the sand. He saw no one. He walked all day, and rested. Rising early, the sun to his back, he followed the coast quite alone. Sometimes as he strode across a sandy beach, just keeping pace with his shadow, he would say: "It is I," and so 'I' became his name.

I made his home in the steep valley that fell away from the bosom of Aripo, dropping to the sea, a place of very great trees, shy deer, many little animals, a host of birds, creatures great and small. I knew no difference between himself and all that lived about him, and there was no difference. He would lie upon his back and gaze up into the sky. Sometimes he would see a star blaze in the blue; and at night, from the branches of a big silk cotton tree, in his dreams he would fly, catching glimpses of himself in other times, and in strange places.

Once, between midnight and dawn, he dreamed a cool wind blew about his head, and he saw before him a big macajuel, its forked tongue slipping silently in and out of its mouth.

"Take it easy," said the snake. "I have come to tell you this: once, long ago when the moon was new, it sent a message to its children, the Aruacs, to say that in the same way it died and was renewed, so too the people of this world would die and be renewed. But by the time I reached here and started to tell the people, I really forgot the whole message—and the people themselves, they are so stupid, up to now they think it is only the moon that is renewed, and for living things—when you dead you done."

"The power in seeing is believing," said I.

"So true," said the snake.

"Did you tell some and not others?" asked I.

"Yes," said the snake.

"Is that why you have a forked tongue?"

"Yes," said the macajuel. "That is the damn thing self."

The days had become dry, so hot that the rivers and pools grew small. The trees with few leaves became gaunt with a heat that felt like it would explode. It did. Huge fires bellowed through the forest, driving all but the trees before it. In the terror of their inferno, they stood rooted to the spot, flaming branches tossing in the wind, tongues of flame. I felt their pain as keenly as he had marvelled at their majesty and great age. He ran screaming into the sea. In fright, he spent the night at the water's edge, but, as day dawned, he thought to himself: "Why should I be afraid? Is it not all the same, and I not one with everything, both the fire and the inflamed?"

After that, I would catch a glimpse of a form reflected in the mountain pools, among the stones and leaves that lay on the bottom. Sometimes, in the sky, or mixed between trees, sky, a darting bird, a cloud, he would glimpse a passing shape.

He was not afraid, he knew that all was I—endless reflections of himself upon the earth and in the sky.

Birds, animals and trees enjoyed the interest that I took in them, and, as the years went by, I became their guardian and friend—mending wings and broken bones, standing godfather for the many young creatures who found themselves orphaned, creating a lasting bond between mankind and the children of the Earth. And the more he stretched his hands in kindness to the creatures, the more he became blessed. Fortune and wisdom were his constant companions, and I forged a link between Heaven above and the Earth beneath.

Wisest and swiftest of creatures on this island was the Humming Bird—bright, flighty, jewel of the forest. The bird, she became I's eyes and ears. And I, I became a Humming Bird. Morning would find him flying, a bright arc through the forest, stopping here and now, swiftly hovering, piercing flowers, absorbing juices, sparkling sugars, giving with his beauty and flight to all creation what he took in sweet energy from it.

Brightly balanced above a shining, streaming mountain pool, the sun turning his speeding wings from red to green and back to red again, I saw below a wondrous sight. Basking, beautiful she lay—her upper body as finely made as I's, and from her waist she had a fish's shape, long and slight. Swift as light, I landed and turned to mortal form. Startled, the creature dived into the pool. I followed, and, much to his delight, found many others of her kind. Strange, beautiful, always swift and silent, they swam just out of his grasp, elusive as a half-remembered daydream, a smell of flowers, or a mountain pool.

Time and time again, I would find himself in this river of the ladies, the Madames, as he called them—the Ladies of the Bay, ever-singing silent songs on still afternoons, sitting on the water's edge in the sunlight, lingering for a golden moment, a flash of green—gone! Nothing but a big morne bleu rising in the sunbeams.

"Did you see a fish jump?"

"Yes, but it did not go back in again!"

The world went by. I, the only dreamer on the scene, was sharply etched against all horizons. I became all things. I called many things by their names—Tucuche and Tarcarib, so to be known ever after. I walked across mountains and savannahs, north, south, east, west, and wherever he went, made a name for himself. Some of these names still remain.

Once I became a tree, a great immortelle towering into the sky. "Papa Bois," he called that wood. A big rise!

"What is the most precious, the most fragile?" he asked the bird buzzing in his vermillion branches.

"Ti Marie, Ti Marie," the Humming Bird replied.

And, as morning broke, the pouis shocked into yellow, and a rolling stone came to a halt. For Papa Bois had come to Iere, a great immortelle in full bloom, standing on the top of El Tucuche. I cried: "Ti Marie, where is she?"

"What he say?" said the bird, busy with her nests. "What he say?"

"Ti Marie, which part she living?" said I, as he bellowed through his branches. But she flew away.

"The wind," she thought. "Willy-nilly, blowing."

"Stop so!" said I as he hurried on his way, and to this day "Qu'est-ce qu'il dit?" says the kiskidee.

A La Diablesse stepped from a great mahogany.

"Hoy," she said in a Bajan accent. "Like you step so fine, which parts you going, brodder mine?"

and the said
the said Court
and took upo
entered into
Premises and
cultivation th
thereof until
thereinafte
remaining
Forsyth
by their said
said Thomas
said Seth a
Judgment a
made to the
William
John Dani
of any pi
Plantation
which was
they were in
for the pay
of any pre

"I looking for T'Marie," said I, starting about him. The forest had grown cold, evening drawing near.

"Like you going far—sit down nuh, take a five!" Now she sounded as though she was from George Street in Port of Spain.

He looked about him and saw a play of energy, a pale grey form, two burning eyes, rising breasts, desire. "Who you?" he asked.

"I am the pain of future years," she answered, quite plainly, in a man's voice, stepping out with her cloven hoof from behind the mahogany, the sound of a chain mingling with the rustle of her petticoats.

"Then you go back where you come from!" I shouted.

"You lucky you get away," answered the La Diablesse. "I looking for a tree to climb."

With the wind in his branches, Papa Bois hurried through the night. As morning soared across the sky, he found her—shy and fragile, a pink puff, leaves closing at his touch, the dew sparkling on her thorn. And they grew together side by side; and ever after have blossomed in the same season.

This beautiful Iere, land of plenty, rivers and mountains—fresh and unspoiled, land of creatures—monkey, lion, fish, serpent and dove, huge butterfly and giant boa constrictor—yellow pouis and silk cotton trees. Sometimes a hawk stopped still, as if painted in the blue sky. Swift humming birds, little Ti Marie, palmiste palms reaching from the forest floor through the tops of tall, thick-canopied trees, to stand out like isolated masts, their branches trailing long, streaming yellow-tail-birds' nests in the wind. All around us were pressed our many seas. We, like a junction of the world—the source of many a distant shore.

Above and below, I reflected in the sea and sky, smiling, sparkling through the leaves on a windy day. There in river water running, the cloudy mountain tops standing like great trees, I was this land. Until one day not even I knew when he was not there anymore.

PAPA BOIS IS THE MOST WIDELY KNOWN of all our folklore characters. He is the old man of the forest and is known by many names, including "Maître Bois" (master of the woods) and "Daddy Bouchon" (hairy man).

Papa Bois appears in many different forms, sometimes as a deer, or in old ragged clothes, sometimes hairy, and though very old, extremely strong and muscular, with cloven hoofs and leaves growing out of his beard. As the guardian of the animals and the custodian of the trees, he is known to sound a cow's horn to warn his friends of the approach of hunters. He doesn't tolerate killing for killing's sake, or the wanton destruction of the forest.

There are many stories of Papa Bois appearing to hunters. Sometimes he turns into a deer that leads the men into the deep forest and then suddenly resumes his true shape, to issue a stern warning before vanishing, leaving the hunters lost, or perhaps compelling them to pay a fine of some sort, such as to marry "Mama Dlo".

If you should meet with Papa Bois be very polite. "Bon jour, vieux Papa," or "Bon Matin, Maître," should be your greeting. If he pauses to pass the time with you, stay cool, and do not look at his feet.

B ON JOUR, MI-JEAN, Mi-Jean the philosopher," said the old man.
"Bon jour, Papa Bois. How come you know my name?" asked Mi-Jean.

"But everyone knows you very well, my friend. High and low, from the cloudy mountain-tops to the villages among the smoke and rum, hasn't everyone heard of Mi-Jean the jurist, the intellectual? Come, sit. Do not be modest. You are among equals."

"I see you have a cow foot, ain't that so?" said Mi-Jean, pointing.

"Yes, yes. A cow foot—you have an eye for detail. Would you like some tobacco? What are you reading?" enquired the old man politely.

"Everything! This book have everything in it you want to know about. Cow foot ... wait ... ah go find it," said Mi-Jean, busy with the index. "Cow heel ..."

from Derek Walcott's *Ti-Jean and his Brothers*

The Soucouyant

GROWING UP IN PORT OF SPAIN in the late 1940s and early 1950s you could still see many aspects of life as lived by its inhabitants sixty or seventy years before as though preserved in a time-capsule. Trams were overtaken by clip-clopping buggies, bread vans made deliveries and hand carts, stacked with bags of sugar, were manoeuvred by three-man teams through the streets. There was horse-drawn transport and lots of bicycles.

The old house on Abercromby Street has long ago become a parking lot. But as a boy I was taken there to meet Madame Juillet.

My aunt Ameline said to me, as we climbed the creaky, dimly lit stairs:

"Be careful what you are thinking. She will read your thoughts."

Have you ever tried to think of nothing?

We met her at the top of the stairs. She had been expecting us. They spoke quickly in patois. The sitting-room was almost bare. A large rocker and an old couch, a low bench and a small wooden chest. Mademoiselle Barth sat on the rocker. Madame Juillet reclined on the couch. My aunt and I sat on the small wooden chest. They were both very old and smelled of vertivert and 'Evening in Paris'.

Mlle. Barth, with Madame Juillet's murmured encouragement, seemed to fall asleep. The other rocked herself gently. I thought of nothing. My aunt had gone there to inquire about Maxim Arneaud, with whom she was in love, and had been for years. As it turned out, she married Charles Loshon, and as Ameline Loshon lived a very happy life.

During the 1940s and 1950s, these two old ladies of Abercromby Street were well known as mediums, voyagers into the spirit world, who were able to solve love triangles, cure maljoe, and were credited in aiding the authorities in finding the remains of Mikey Cipriani in the high mountains of Trinidad's north coast.

It was while on one of these spiritualistic missions that Mlle. Barth in fact met her death. It was well known that old Mrs. Molay of Mayaro was a soucouyant. She didn't trouble the village, and the village didn't trouble her. The problem arose, if you pardon the expression, with her homeward-bound flights. As she grew into her nineties, her sense of direction began to fail. There was, for example, that embarrassing morning when she was discovered naked on top of the water tank in the police station compound. She had put her skin in its protective mortar on the tank. Now her problem was to get down!

The ladies Barth and Juillet were called in to exorcise her soucouyant personality, and that was when the trouble started. Although Mrs. Molay was old and frail, the soucouyant was strong. In the end, Mlle. Barth was savaged and subsequently died. She had been bitten and sucked by the creature on the sole of her foot.

It was said long ago that certain French families brought the vampire tradition to Trinidad. These European vampires intermingled with their enslaved African counterparts, and out of this the soucouyant emerged. The soucouyant makes a pact with the devil, so that she can assume any form. Her first undertaking is to go to a cemetery and dig up a freshly buried corpse and cut out the liver. From this, an oil is made. When this oil is rubbed all over her body, she can slip out of her skin. The skin is kept in a mortar or the hollowed-out trunk of a tree used to parch coffee or ferment cocoa beans.

The soucouyant of Saut d'Eau Island off the north coast is described as a "ball of flame, along she came, flying without a wind". One Monsieur Didier had this to relate:

"One night I was fishing. Suddenly, I saw a globe of fire which appeared far away at the very extremity of the beach where I was and which approached me slowly. I remained absolutely quiet. The globe of fire passed by a few steps away from me, some metres in the air. In the middle of this globe, I saw the face of a woman whom I recognised as a negress from the neighbouring village. When it had passed by, I asked my comrades if they had seen anything. They said they had seen the ball of fire and the face of the woman which it surrounded."

Old people in Paramin can tell you about a soucouyant called Désirée, who on a bet flew to London to steal one of Queen Victoria's gold spoons. However, on her way back with the spoon she "catch a malcadie" over Dent Ma Teteron in the First Bocas, and the spoon fell from her. The large gold spoon to this day lies on that rock in the middle of the First Bocas.

A soucouyant doesn't always suck you. She can pinch you too, or cuff you, and in the morning you will have large black-and-blues that turn a little greenish. After a while, you begin to feel bad, weak, thin, frail, "mager". Your eye sockets are sinking in your head and you are staring at nothing all the time. Then you die.

Sometimes, she is a bat. Sometimes, a hog. There was a soucouyant who used to live at the top of Henry Street. She caused a lot of problems for people coming home late. Ripper Qui Tang's father had a shop. He emptied a hundred-pound bag of rice in front of Rosary Church. The next morning, people saw three big hogs eating the rice. There was another soucouyant who used to live under the washhouse bridge, near to Sunny parlour. She was bad. She used to work the mortuary.

She is the old woman who lives alone at the end of the village road, seldom seen, her house always closed up as she sleeps away the day. As evening draws near, she stirs and sheds her old and wrinkled skin, which she deposits into a mortar that she hides carefully away. Now, as a glowing ball of flame, she rises up through the roof and, with a shrill cry that sets the village dogs to howling, she flies through the night in search of a victim. She sucks his 'life-blood' from him clean.

As the blessed day dawns, she makes a beeline through the forest for her home, finds the mortar with her wretched skin and proceeds to put it on, — but something's wrong, it burns like fire, it seems to shrink and slide away.

"Skin, kin, kin, you na know me, you na know me," she sings, crooning softly, pleading to the wrinkled, dreadful thing. "You na know me, old skin."

Then, with horror, she realises the dreadful thing that has been done: the village boys and men have filled her skin with coarse salt and pepper and will soon come and get her, with a drum of boiling tar, the priest and his silver cross, the church bells — and then, the end.

If you wish to discover who the soucouyant in your village is empty one hundred pounds of rice at the village crossroads, where she will be compelled to pick them up, one grain at a time — that is how you'll know the soucouyant.

The Soucouyant of Sodor

OH, THE SOUCOUYANT OF SODOR, it was an evil sprite;
It slept away the blessed day, it wrought ill all the night.
A ball of flame, along it came, flying without a wind;
And when it burst, that thing accurst, it smote the steersman blind.
Oh, the Soucouyant of Sodor was the terror of the coast!

The "Jesus-Maria-José," she hailed from Pampatar;
It sent her on the cruel rocks, away by Balatá.
The "San Pedro" of Carúpano, the "Santa Fé" of Saïs,
And many more it drove on shore and perished in like wise.
Oh, the Soucouyant of Sodor, it was a gruesome ghost!

There was a crone in Sodor town, this fiend inhabited.
She slept away the blessed day, at night she lay for dead;
Now they have taken that lifeless crone, and put fire to her toes;
A burning match they made her clutch; and sore they wrung her nose.
Oh Soucouyant of Sodor, 'tis time to be at home!

They racked her here, they racked her there, her blood was all a-froth...
A ball of flame a-flying came, and flew in at her mouth.
Then sore, then sore that crone 'gan roar, for mercy sore she cried;
But they have taken the miscreant and drowned her in the tide.
And the Soucouyant of Sodor since then has ceased to roam!

(from *Legends of the Bocas*, A.D. Russell, 1922)

The Ligahoo

I REMEMBER HIM WELL; the first time we met I was "pelting" home, up Hermitage Road in Belmont.

It must have been near Christmas, because it was not that late, but it was already dark. It may have been a Thursday; the street was empty because the shops, Chinee John, Papits and Cecils, were shut half-day. I had gone to "Missing Ball" parlour for comics and had run right into him.

Tall, black, dressed in a black suit, he smelled like mothballs. I mostly remember his eyes, bulging red. By the time I got home, grandma was waiting in the gallery: "You meet him?"

She had seen him. "Serve you right."

That night I could feel his eyes. He had seen me. He knew me. Tantie Rosa said he was on his way to Lapeyrouse to dig up some grave dirt with a big black penny.

He was the science man who could read the "teetalbey" on the black arts. And dealt with the devil. He could turn into any beast and roam the streets at night. Sometimes people saw him by Reform Lane, a coffin on his head and chains dragging behind him. In everyday life he was a practicing obeah man and a genius at maiming or killing anybody. People say sometimes he was so tall that his head disappeared into the clouds. "Take care you get 'too-tool-bay'," said Grandma. "Say your prayers." I did, twice.

Obeah is the general term used for the system of magic and sorcery in Trinidad. The word is African in origin, according to anthropologist Melville Herskovits. In Trinidad, most overt African religious practices were suppressed during the period of slavery, and it is generally believed that obeah is made up, basically, of fragments of rituals and remembered religious practices of African cults that were brought to Trinidad at the end of the 18th century. This was further reinforced by fresh information brought straight from Africa in the 1850s by the Freed Africans; that is, people taken off Portuguese slavers on the high seas by the British Royal Navy and "freed" in Trinidad.

The Power of the Obeah Man

————— ⦿⧢⧢ —————

WAS AND STILL IS SIGNIFICANT. In the old days, this had to do with life and death. It was said that the one on our street had sold his son's soul to the devil for wealth and power but later reneged on the deal, and that is why he had died badly. Every culture possesses a tradition of black magic. In Europe, for example, the vampire, the werewolf and the undead are now big business in books, movies and games.

Long ago, obeah was very common, so much so that the British authorities would sentence you to a jail term for it. But that did not stop the practice. As boys we ventured into "his" yard to retrieve the only corkball we had. Bush surrounded the old wooden house. There was an air of abandonment. His lights had been cut. While the others searched, I peeped in through the jealousies. I saw a dusty old room, old books and papers scattered on the floor, broken furniture, a single bed in the middle of the drawing room, a big white "posy" (chamberpot) on a bench, bottles and a pitch-oil lamp. I could smell it. A pile of dirt lay on a newspaper in the middle of the floor.

"You want to see? Come." A hand rested on my shoulder. I felt my soul quake as I looked up into his red eyes blazing in the mid afternoon.

"No," I quivered.

"Then go home."

I fled.

"Myth is the twilight speech of an old man to a boy. The speech of an elder in the twilight of his life is not his history, but a legacy; he speaks, not to describe matter, but to demonstrate meaning."

Thus writes Maya Deren in her excellent book *Voodoo Gods*. An old man speaks of his past for the purpose of the future. His purpose selects his memories. As Deren writes:

"He remembers that which has been, according to what could and should be. From the material circumstances of his experience he plots, in retrospect, the adventure for the mind which is the myth."

It is with this in mind that I approached a fascinating collection of stories written in the mid-19th century by a visitor to Trinidad and Tobago. They were told by Hersketh J. Bell, who spent many years in the British Colonial Service in the West Indies and was subsequently Governor of the island of Mauritius. Here are two:

The Man Ligahoo

"CHRISTMAS MORNING! yet the trees are green, and butterflies are fluttering in the air. As I ride along the winding path, returning from a refreshing dip in the sea, I can hardly realize that this is winter! that on the other side of the Atlantic it is miserably cold, perhaps snow on the ground, and probably most people indoors, shivering round a fire; while here—a lovely, cool, spice-laden breeze is wafted down from the mountains yonder—the sun shines down out of a bright blue sky, and humming-birds of gorgeous colouring flit over the scented black sage bushes.

The path, now and then shaded with clumps of feathery bamboo or bushy tufted groo-groo palms, skirts a hillside covered with waving sugar-canes, while in the distance, I can see the deep blue ocean, stretching away till sea and sky melt in a haze.

My companion, a genial French Roman Catholic priest, rides a few paces ahead, his bathing towel slung round his neck, and in his mouth a never-missing cigarette. An "Obeah bottle" hanging from a mango-tree draws my attention to the subject which interests me so much, and riding up, I ask my companion what he can tell me about the superstitions of the country.

"Ah, my dear fellow, I can't remember half I hear and notice on these ever-present superstitions of the people, but I assure you that it is one of the greatest obstacles I meet with in my work among the parishioners; these foolish but so deeply rooted beliefs of theirs in the power of Obeah and witchcraft meet me at every turn, and after talking for hours, and trying to prove to them how ridiculous and senseless all these ideas are, I only obtain a seeming acquiescence, and make no lasting impression.

"I have tried everything to combat the baneful influence, and endeavoured to make them ashamed of their ignorance and credulity, but with precious little effect. I have even adopted the Japanese custom of punishing a whole street for the misdeeds of one criminal living in it, by refusing the sacraments for a time to a whole family, if a member of it be known to be dabbling in Obeah—all to small purpose.

"This reminds me that, only the other day, I was riding to see a sick person living on the other side of the parish, when I happened to pass a small wooden house, before which a number of people were congregated, all talking together and evidently much excited in their minds about something inexplicable. On asking what was the matter, I was told that the owner of the house was lying dead, and that he was an Obeah man who had lived quite alone in the place for many years, and that there was consequently no one willing to undertake the job of looking after the corpse and burying it.

"In fact, no one would go inside the hut at all, as it was affirmed that His Satanic Majesty was there in person looking after the body of the Obeah man, which now undoubtedly belonged to him.

"To allay their alarm, I got off my horse, and with the assistance of a couple of men broke open the door and entered the hut. Lying on a wooden stretcher was the body of the unfortunate individual, whose death must have occurred a good many hours before, and the body was in urgent need of burial, so after scolding the people for their cowardice I prevailed on them to see about a coffin and other details as quickly as possible. It was, however, only in evident fear and trembling that any of them would enter the room, and the slightest noise would make them start and look towards the door, in the expectation of seeing "le diable en personne" coming to claim his property.

"The dirty little room was littered with the Obeah man's stock in trade. A number of vials containing some sort of unholy liquor were lying ready to be handed over to some foolish negro in exchange for their weight in silver. In every corner were found the implements of his trade: rags, feathers, bones of cats, parrots' beaks, dogs' teeth, broken bottles, grave dirt, rum, and egg-shells. Examining further, we found under the bed a large conarie or earthen jar, containing an immense number of round balls of earth or clay of various dimensions, large and small, whitened on the outside and fearfully and wonderfully compounded. Some seemed to contain hair and rags and were strongly bound round with twine; others were made with skulls of cats, stuck round with human or dogs' teeth and glass beads. There were also a lot of egg-shells and numbers of little bags filled with a farrago of rubbish.

"In a little tin canister I found the most valuable of the sorcerer's stock, namely, seven bones belonging to a rattlesnake's tail—these I have known sell for five dollars each, so highly valued are they as amulets or charms—in the same box was about a yard of rope, no doubt intended to be sold for hangman's cord, which is highly prized by the negroes, the owner of a piece being supposed to be able to defy bad luck.

"Rummaging further, I pulled out from under the thatch of the roof an old preserved-salmon tin, the contents of which showed how profitable was the trade of the Obeah man. It was stuffed full of five-dollar bank-notes, besides a number of handsome twenty-dollar gold pieces, the whole amounting to a considerable sum, which I confess I felt very reluctant to seal up and hand over to the Government, the Obeah man not being known to have heirs. I then ordered the people to gather up all the rubbish, which was soon kindled and blazing away merrily in front of the hut, to the evident satisfaction of the bystanders, who could hardly be persuaded to handle the mysterious tools of Obeah.

"The man, I heard, had a great reputation for sorcery, and I was assured that even persons who would never be suspected of encouraging witchcraft had been known to come from a distance to consult him or purchase some love-spell.

"The secret of their reputation and frequent success in finding out robberies, which is also a part of their profession, is most likely due to a good memory and a system of cross-questioning all those who come to consult them, and it is also very probable that they possess a knowledge of numerous tricks and deceits handed down to them by their African progenitors, with which they astonish even educated persons and perform wonders which would almost convert one to a belief in magic."

Over the years, the pure African system of obeah has been altered to include the western magical tradition, the use of magical books, such as those by Albertus Magnus, and also the mail order catalogue of deLaurence *Books of Magick* of Chicago.

East Indians too have a tradition of black magic sorcery. They call it "ojah" or "indra jal". There are books on witchcraft such as *Kautak Ratan Bhandar*.

Obeah can be used either for harm or for good. The most common purposes for which people resort to this magic are to cure sicknesses or to make enemies sick, to make money, to get a better job, to win a case in court, to cure someone of spirit possession and as love magic.

In the old days, there were lots of rules with regard to the dead. Firstly, you were told that when a corpse was leaving the house, the water in which it had been bathed must be thrown out after it, or else the ghost will haunt the house. For the same reason it must be carried out feet first, otherwise he or she may well return.

Want to see a Loup Gahou? Get some "dog yampee" (mucus from their eyes), put it in your own eye and look through a keyhole at midnight. After dark, never stand in a doorway in such a way to prevent another person from passing through; for there may be a ghost who wants to pass, and it may touch you. Then you feel a sudden sickness in the region of your stomach, get goose bumps and feel a chill. Oh, and never call your children's names out loud at dusk, the Duennes will hear you and steal the name and call your children away ...

The Woman Ligahoo

IN THE 1860s, A FRENCH PRIEST came to Trinidad, where he had been sent by the Archbishop to take charge of a parish far in the interior of the island. There was no presbytery, and he had to make shift until he could build one. He moved into a small wooden house, of which one room was occupied by an old coloured woman, who lived there with a little girl.

This woman was looked on with a good deal of dread by the people, being supposed to possess knowledge of "a good many unholy tricks", as the French priest put it. It was confidently hoped that his near neighbourhood would do her good, and at all events induce the old woman to be seen now and then at church, which was a sign of respectability in those years.

When taking possession of his part of the house, the priest was shown her room, and noticed that it contained some really handsome pieces of the massive furniture so much esteemed by creoles in those days. A tremendous family four-poster, with heavy, handsomely turned pillars, stood in one corner near a ponderous mahogany wardrobe, and various other bits of furniture pretty well filled the little room. The door of her apartment opened to the priest's room, which

and the said
the said Court
and took upon
entered into
Premises and
cultivation the
thereof until
thereinafter
remaining due
Forsyth the
by their said
said Thomas
said Debh and
Judgment and
made to them
William
John Daniel
of any prior
Plantation an
which was due
they were with
for the paym

she had to pass through every time she went out of the house. This was an unpleasant arrangement, but was shortly to be remedied by having another door made in her room leading outside.

It was never to come to that, though. The night after the priest had taken possession, he heard a monotonous sound through the partition, as if someone were crooning a sing-song chant. This continued for over an hour, and more than once he felt inclined to rap at the partition and beg the old dame to shut up her incantations, but it finally acted as a lullaby and he soon dropped asleep.

The next morning, having got up and dressed, he noticed that all was perfectly silent next door, and on listening attentively he failed to hear a sound. He feared something had gone wrong, but noticed that the door leading to his room had not been opened, as a chair he had placed against it was in precisely the same position as he had left it. He then knocked at her door several times, but obtained no answer; fearing an accident had happened, he opened the door, and as it swung back on its hinges he was astonished to see the room perfectly empty and evidently swept clean.

On examining the room carefully, he found it had only two small windows besides the door leading into his room. From that day to this neither he nor anyone living in that district has ever seen or heard anything of that woman or of her little girl. How she moved all her heavy furniture out of that little room, has ever remained an inexplicable mystery. One man could not have moved the wardrobe alone, and even if the old woman had had strength enough to carry the furniture away, she never could have dragged it through the priest's room without disturbing him! However, these are the facts of the case, and nobody has ever been able to explain them.

The Ligahoo or "Loup Garou" is the shape changer of Trinidad's folklore. This phenomenon is usually associated with an old magic-dealing man of a district who is both feared and respected, not only for his power to change his form to that of a vicious animal, but also for his power over nature. He can lay curses and extend protection; from him, charms and bush medicine are also readily available. "Long ago, in Tobago, he could make trees come down so that he would be able to get at the mangoes," as the Mighty Shadow once explained to me.

At times the apparition may take the form of a coffin being carried through the streets and the clank of chains is distinctly heard. A single man may bear it on his head, protected by a giant "phantome". If by chance the coffin and its gruesome attendant were used to facilitate the uninterrupted transportation of bush rum, this effect would virtually ensure its safe passage.

The La Diablesse

A N ENCOUNTER WHICH REVEALS much of the character of the La Diablesse was related to me by an old man, perhaps now a dead man.

Mount Diable in central Trinidad might be the home of the La Diablesse stories that coloured the imagination of turn-of-the-century Trinidad. She may well be a syncretic creation, combining the West African goddess Erzulie, tragic mistress turned vengeful, slave concubine, beautiful, desirous, feminine presence, the ever young seductress. As Maya Deren describes her in her book *The Voodoo Gods*, she is Marinette, the wife of Ti Jean Petro, and stands for the "capacity to conceive beyond reality, to desire beyond adequacy, to create beyond need".

The La Diablesse, like Erzulie, is not a mother goddess in the sense that she is the mother of human beings. Instead, she is the mother of the human being's myth of life, of life's meaning.

It may be that she, as a philosophical principle rather than a ghost, was brought to Trinidad in the 1780s by Afro-Franco-Creole slaves from Grenada, St. Lucia, Haiti and the other islnds of the French Antilles.

As the "devil woman", the La Diablesse possesses one cloven hoof. Her other foot is elegantly shod. From her slave heritage, there is an old iron chain that girds her waist and trails after her. Other than that, she is very elaborately dressed in the ancient costume of the French islands: a brilliant madras turban, chemise with half-sleeves and much embroidery and lace, several gold necklaces made up of small gold nuggets, huge "eggshell" earrings and many pins of gold trembling in her turban. In fact, the Erzulie cult too is preceded by an elaborate ceremony of dressing and toilette. Soaps, perfumes, mirrors, silk handkerchiefs, and jewelry are consecrated to her in the Voodoo belief.

The sound of her chain mingling with the rustle of her petticoats is the first thing that a man notices of a La Diablesse's appearance, even before seeing her. She carries a bag tied to her waist. In it are the human bones of her previous life and the dirt of the grave in which she was once buried. There are also old English pennies, black with age, her passage money, as well as sea shells, symbols of her travels.

In Trinidad, La Diablesse is the spirit of the woman wronged, and as such awaits the male predator so as to take vengeance for transgressions against women.

As she stops a man in the gathering dusk, the odour of seduction swirls about her. He rises with desire and follows her into a forest glen. Sometimes his broken body will be found; sometimes he comes back from the glen possessed by a strange lunacy.

La Diablesse may appear at midday as a tall, handsome creole woman, who, with swinging gait and erect stature, passes through a cane or cocoa field and catches the eye of the man who had wronged her sex. He then follows her, and, never able to catch up with her—her feet hardly touching the ground—finds himself lost, bewildered, far from home, and to his horror he discovers that his form no longer casts a shadow. He is never quite himself again.

The La Diablesse can manifest herself from age to age in some old creole families, who in ancient days were traumatised with brutality or terrorised to madness by obeah. She then can take revenge on the descendants of those who brought her to the condition of the vengeful one.

The Curse of the La Diablesse

1882. Nobody lived in the old house anymore. It was so old that it leaned in a sinking kind of way into the soft, wet earth. It stood on a knoll which formed part of Mount Diable.

Nobody except for Mayotte could remember why that outcrop and that twisting mountain road had been named for the devil. She was so old that she still bore the scars of slavery on her body. She was so old that she could remember a childhood close to the Grand Etang in Grenada almost one hundred years ago, coming to Trinidad with all the other la Tuilerie slaves and fighting with the jungle in central Trinidad to clear out a new plantation to suffer on.

She was so old that she remembered the Carib people being buried sitting, their hands around their knees, in small holes all about the place. She was so old that she could remember when the white people lived in the old house at the top of Mount Diable Road in Tamana.

The young boy with the Spanish hat who had come to visit her wanted to know about folklore.

"Folklore, folklore," she said, treating it like a foreign word. It was, in fact, alien to her mind. "You have to sleep with fowls to know if they snore."

"Tell me about the La Diablesse," said the young man. He was no older than 17 or 18.

She watched him good. Her hip was paining her—rain was coming.

"Come back in the morning." Disappointed, the young man left her.

The old slave barracks at the back of the house were now empty except for her. She blew out the pitch oil lamp and lay down. The comforting smell of the lamp filled her room and she fell fast asleep. The moonlight crept through the open door, across the wooden floor and up the wall. The rain had not come. Later, Mayotte lay awake on the rumpled, tepid sheets, smelling her old body, sweat running down her neck. In the darkness, just when sleep was about to cast its dark cloak once more upon her, she saw it. There was a movement around the bottom of the bed. To her shock, a female form emerged, half in her mind's eye, and turned with staring countenance to her.

"My God," she breathed as she looked into her own face. "It must be hundreds of years old."

Hers was the trembling, toothless mouth, the yellow eyes, sightless, the shrinking body numb with years, scaly feet, decrepit toes, the phlegm of death rattling piteously in a throat that bowed an almost bald old head towards her.

The boy in the Spanish hat would never hear her La Diablesse folklore. He came the next morning, just after they had found Mayotte dead. Disappointed once again, he turned his horse away from the barrack rooms, now filled with the curiosity of the villagers, and rode up to the old, empty plantation house.

He decided to explore its crumbling interior a bit. After all, it had been his father's house, the house that his father had lived in before he had migrated with his mother and his older sister to New Orleans. He had been born in that city, but had decided to spend a holiday in Trinidad with his father's school friend. His host, in fact, had told him to go to Mayotte and learn about the La Diablesse.

The young man skipped up the creaking front steps, two at a time. Above them was a withered carved sign spelling "etit Trou"—the P had become illegible.

The old drawing-room was empty. Little clouds of dust rose at his feet with every step, glittering in the sunlight that filtered through the rotten jealousies. He looked about him. An open doorway showed a flight of stairs. He mounted these quickly, before he could change his mind, and came along a long corridor. Three empty rooms, the doors to which had gone. The fourth one, the smallest, a child's room, contained the frame of a small iron four-poster bed and a broken-down cupboard. One door of the cupboard had fallen from its hinge, and he saw that a small tin box was inside. Quickly, he took it, and left the house.

Back at his host's house, he took the tin box out of his bag and opened it. In it was the petrified leg of some hoofed animal, a small white porcelain boy doll, an ancient bible, a large key, a roll of parchment and a pile of old manuscripts. It all looked as though it had not been touched for many years.

Curious, the young man started to read the handwritten pages. They were written in French. Some pages seemed to be missing, as the narrative began in the middle of a sentence, in a scrawling, messy script.

"... when suddenly a female creature, a spirit, a goddess—Erzulie—a woman, entered your field of vision. You would desire her. That she would come to you at that particular time in your devotion, in your prayer, with your chaplet in hand, would make her more irresistible. She would be the other, the insurmountable other. She is what you expelled in prayer, but she returned, more compelling yet, suspended in air. Resist her! She, hateful, mocking, grabbing your thighs, pulling your garments! This creature, touching you, humiliating you. A gorgeous woman, wide hips, long hands, will ..."

Here, the handwriting ended abruptly. On another sheet of the same paper, the same handwriting had written an account of something, but in a much neater, clearer hand. It was titled "An account of the French family of Mercier de la Tuilerie in Trinidad".

"Pierre Louis Charles Mercier de la Tuilerie took his family to La Trinité in 1791. A massive black slave carried his wife, Marie-Ange, in his arms through the mud and mangroves towards the shore. He then went back to the brigantine's long boat and brought his daughter Clémence and their belongings. A light rain fell.

"De la Tuilerie had acquired the plantation Petit Trou at Tamana in the hope of escaping the sad depredations that had afflicted him in Grenada.

"Clémence de la Tuilerie grew into a young woman of easy grace and calm demeanour. Like many young women of her class and time, she looked forward to marriage. Isolated from society as she was, but never lonely, she received an education from her father in the classics and could speak Spanish and Italian with the same ease as her native French. She mastered the intricacies of the Spanish guitar and loved to watch the slaves dance the belair. She would join them in their cropover festival dressed in foulard and madras, wearing a wide, colourful skirt over many lace petticoats.

"On her 19th birthday, the midday downpour had become a terrible storm by the early evening. The wind was hurling the branches of the giant trees to the ground. The rain was falling in blinding sheets. Lightning cracked the sky, thunder boomed with the sound of a cannon.

"Hit by one bolt of lightning, Clémence's parents died as they were attempting to save the kitchen stores. She found herself alone on the plantation with the slaves and Monsieur Paul Guillet, the close-by neighbour. Clémence was well off; her father, a prudent man, had secured his fortune.

"By the following year, with the help of M. Guillet, she had assumed control of Petit Trou. It is hard to say at what stage Petit Trou started to control her. Perhaps it was that she was dependent on Mi Jean, the headman, to implement her orders. The reins of power had begun to slip from her hands.

"To control Mi Jean, she had to rely on Ma Lou, her nanny, who had brought her up. Ma Lou was a Yoruba woman in her late fifties. For a slave, she held much power as a result of her position in the household. It was she who put Mayotte, then a young woman like Clémence, to watch over the mistress of the house.

"There was a stillness over the plantation. In the heat of the day, a gang of slaves raped Clémence and killed her, slicing her throat and mutilating her young body before setting the house ablaze. Ma Lou saved the house, but not before Clémence's body had been terribly burnt. She herself succumbed to her wounds shortly after.

"Later on, the property of Petit Trou was bought by Paul Guillet from the moneylender Fatio, who held a mortgage."

The young man stopped reading. He turned the pages in his hand to find the end of the manuscript. The last inscribed page was undersigned with:

"Jean Guillet, in the year of Our Lord 1855."

He swallowed. His throat felt very dry. The heat of the afternoon had made him drowsy and hot. Jean Guillet was the name of his great-grandfather.

Why had Jean written the strange account of the prayer, when apparently he was tormented by the passions of the flesh, possessed of a wild and raving desire? What had the hoof, the doll, to do with these manuscripts? He leafed through the old bible. On the fly leaf somebody had inscribed "1789". In a very fine script, the front and back had been filled with years of baptisms, births and deaths in French families.

Utterly weary now, the young man put everything back into the tin box and fell asleep on his bed. Later that evening, he was awoken to have dinner with his hosts. After dinner, he excused himself early, took a lamp to his room, and continued to read the manuscript by the glow of the lamplight.

"... It was several days before the chief constable arrived at Petit Trou. Already the bush was creeping back. The place seemed wilder. The air was still. 'They went into the forest,' M. Guillet told the constable. 'By now they must be in Moruga, looking for a boat to go down the main. What a terrible thing, terrible.'

"The chief constable and his party stayed the night, and the next morning saddled their ponies and left early for Arima. Clémence and Ma Lou were buried in the garden next to Clémence's parents' grave. Over the years, the samaan tree that shaded the cemetery grew gigantic, and except for the rusting iron railing it was difficult to know exactly where the four graves were. The estates around Petit Trou prospered and the slave cottages that had been built nearby grew into little villages.

"After Paul Guillet died in 1840, I, Jean Pierre, his son, ran the estate at Petit Trou. Life had changed. Slavery had been abolished, and we had to hire workers to work in the sugar and cocoa fields. It was a most difficult time for me, my wife Gwendolyn and our son Charles. One Abbé La Geoff had become parish priest, and to him I confided my story.

"My father, whom I loved and admired, had become a very strange and most peculiar person as he grew older. He was a very troubled man. There were times when he appeared mad—his appearance, the manner in which he kept himself, his ravings, his disappearances from the estate to go into the high woods, his suspicions of constantly being spied upon. Eventually, he died at the old house in Petit Trou, very mad.

"After his death, in going through his things, I found a hoof, a porcelain doll from the previous century, and a de la Tuilerie bible. It was not long after that my own visions and a

and the said
the said Court
and took upon
entered into
Premises and
cultivation the
thereof until
thereinafter
remaining due
Forsyth the
by their said
said Thomas
said Deth and
Judgment and
made to them
William
John Daniel
of any prior
Plantation an
which was due
they were will
for the paym

feeling of panic commenced. I decided to go to the Abbé, and I took along with me my father's parchment inscribed in Spanish, which I didn't speak. He promised to read it, and we parted.

"Some weeks later, I went to visit the Abbé. When I arrived, he was praying in front of the shrine in his little church in Tortuga, which contained a Black Madonna of Montserrat. It was a replica of a statue at Montserrat in Spain, and had been brought to Trinidad probably a century ago by Capuchin monks, missionaries to the Amerindians.

"After he had finished praying, the Abbé La Geoff came up to me and invited me into his presbytery.

'You realise that this parchment contains the confession to a terrible crime?' he asked me.

"I was surprised. We were sitting at the open window looking out on the quiet country road bathed in sunlight. Little girls, bright red ribbons in their hair, and a group of old ladies were walking home from church.

'My son, in arranging for Clémence's murder by the slaves, your father acquired Petit Trou at a very cheap price. His guilt haunted him in his life and to his death. May his soul rest in peace...'

"I looked at him and almost didn't dare to speak. But I did.

'I have seen her... Clémence.'

'Is this why you have come?' asked the Abbé.

'Yes,' I answered. 'Mayotte, our housekeeper, a former slave of the de la Tuileries', had told me of the terrible deaths, and warned me of how the cocoa would fail, and of how the workers who came to Mount Diable would become peculiar and queer. But she never spoke of my father.'

'Are you afraid?' asked the Abbé.

"I am very afraid. Afraid for my own sanity, because I have seen her too, Clémence, with her rustling petticoats, with her hoof, have been almost seduced by her animal smell. The things in my father's belongings brought these strange visions to my consciousness. I am afraid for my Gwendolyn, for Charles. I am taking Abbé La Geoff's advice, and will sell the estate and go away, to the United States of America. I will leave these things and this account in the house at Petit Trou, so they shall not haunt me anywhere else.

"Jean Guillet, in the year of Our Lord 1855."

The young man's eyes burned. He had come out to Trinidad to find his roots. His grandfather, Charles, had only known fond stories of his early childhood in central Trinidad. It was he who had told him to go and find out from Mayotte about the La Diablesse, a very important folklore story in Mount Diable.

The young man in the Spanish hat did not go back to New Orleans, not for a long, long time. He stayed in Trinidad and as a mature man married a much younger woman. Only afterwards, he eventually went back to the United States with his young wife and baby daughter. Had he too been seduced by Clémence's ghost? Mayotte had not wanted to tell the poor child, ignorance is bliss. She died instead. In vain—the story of the curse was far from over.

Having been born and raised in the U.S. by a single mother, another young man came to Trinidad to visit, this time in the 1940s. It was a time of war, and he—barely 22—fell in with the soldiers and sailors from his native country who were stationed here.

Walking home to his boarding house in Newtown late one evening, a strange woman attracted his attention. She was young—or perhaps not so young, who knows. She was dressed in an old-fashioned style, staring at him with her eyelids lowered in a seductive manner, but staring nonetheless, you know how it goes.

He thought her to be a prostitute, because her dress was cut so low as to reveal one breast almost entirely.

Walking more quickly, since he had no intention to speak to her, the young man felt the urge to turn around. He fought it with all the good upbringing he could muster, but the urge became stronger. Two houses from his own, in a pool of light from the street lamp, he turned—and found her face two inches away, her eyes locked into his. Her bosom exuded a smell of leaves and perfume. Her voice sounded like a cry of agony and the purr of a cat. As she turned around to lead him away, her face never turned with her body, but continued to keep his gaze locked. There was the 'thump' of hoof and the sound of a chain mingling with the rustle of petticoats.

He woke from his trance as an old man, sitting on a stool in the Pelican pub. The curfew of 1990 prevented him, along with several other patrons of the bar, from leaving. That is where I met him, and during the long night of looting and shooting going on outside, his garbled story came out, much to the amusement of everybody caught in the Pelican for the night of curfew.

"I have that old tin chest," he said. Dawn was breaking. "Would you like to have it, eventually? I would hate to throw it away, it belongs to the island."

"No, thank you, Mister Guillet," I said. "I have enough old rubbish already."

Strangely enough, another story of a La Diablesse was related to me by my grandmother when she was still alive; I must have been a teenager. She told me of a woman, Clara, who had been a school friend of her mother. As a little girl of perhaps five or six, Clara was walking along a street in Newtown at the hand of her nanny. Suddenly, she felt intimidated by a strange man whom they encountered in the street. He was loitering opposite the entrance to a barrack yard, and was dressed in black clothes, wearing a black Spanish-style hat. His eyes were shaded

by the broad rim of his hat, but Clara could clearly make out their colour: they were RED.

"Don't look at him." The nanny pressed her hand so hard that tears welled up in Clara's eyes, and dragged her along with a firm step. As they were just about to pass the man, a woman stepped from the barrack yard opposite. Clara didn't dare to look up, but could clearly hear chains clinking and taffetta rustling. The little girl smelt strange, strong perfume and rotting leaves.

"Don't look," hissed the nanny.

Hurriedly, they passed in the middle of the deserted street between the man and the woman. Clara was terrified. When they had passed them, and reached quite a few houses further down, she could hear the woman's shrill laughter:

"This time you get away! This time, you hear! You just wait! She save you, but not forever! Not all of you, not ever!"

Later on, Clara got married to a much older man from a respectable family. She had a daughter with him and they migrated to the United States, where her husband had been born. Their daughter later had an illegitimate son in the 1920s. Only after the wedding Clara discovered an old-fashioned Spanish felt hat, broad-brimmed, in her husband's armoire, which made her remember the incident when she was a child.

Long after the coup of 1990, I started to wonder whether the two stories that had been told to me almost 40 years apart were related. Could it be that the La Diablesse Clara saw was the same that had put a hex on Mr. Guillet whom I met in the Pelican, because he was in fact the grandson of the man with the Spanish hat, the first male in the Guillet family since him? Did Clara prevent her future husband from being taken by a La Diablesse, only for her grandson, when he came back to Trinidad, to fall under the spirit's spell?

Who knows. Maybe I was just following my own creole heritage, weaving together a tale, weaving, weaving ...

A Note on Witch Tales

THE "OLD WOMAN OF THE VILLAGE" is a traditional evil character in the folklore of many cultures. Where does she come from? A socio-historical explanation may be ventured here.

Women naturally live longer than men, and more often than not a woman lived to great age whereas her husband died younger, in war, because of sickness, or in an accident. Old people were more often than not women, not men.

Furthermore, in traditional cultures, women did not enjoy the same rights as men. There are many accounts of widows being total outcasts from village life—the people of the village coveted her land and her possessions for themselves, especially if the woman had no sons of her own to protect her.

So the ugly, wrinkled and lonesome old woman was a burden on village life, just another mouth to feed. Because she was a woman, nobody was interested in her personal life experience and wisdom. When she had no protectors, people invented witch stories around her, and in the end killed her, sharing her possessions, her land, her house and her livestock amongst themselves.

So take the Soucouyant and La Diablesse stories with a grain of—coarse—salt!

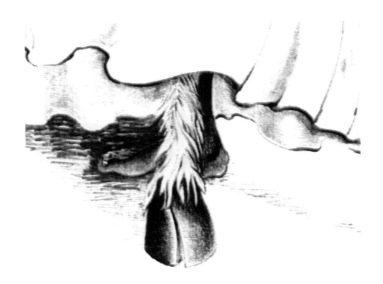

Ti Jeanne's Last Laundry

MAMAN DLO, WHOSE NAME is derived from the French "maman de l'eau", which means "mother of the water" is one of the protectresses of the forest and its rivers, waterfalls and pools.

It was towards the end of the rainy season. Ti Jeanne, who lived with her grandmother in Blanchisseuse, went to the river pool with her basket of laundry.

She tied up her skirt around her waist, waded into the water, and her round, brown arms moved rhythmically up and down as she beat the laundry against a stone. Her voice rang out in the forest, mingling with the song of birds high up in the trees, the screech of parrots and the more mysterious sounds of the forest. Whap, whap went the wet laundry.

"La rene, la rene, la rene rivé," sang Ti Jeanne.

"Qu'est-ce qu'elle dit?" asked the kiskidee, who never really understands anything. Ti Jeanne worked away in the solitude of the ravine, the sun travelled its course across the sky, and when the last piece of laundry was washed and wrung and laid out to bleach on the stones, Ti Jeanne sat down, splashing her feet in the water, and looking at her reflection in the water of a small, clear pool, turning this way and that to catch a glimpse of her pretty features.

"Who's that singing so fine?" came a hissing, creaky voice from the dark greenery. "Who's that splashing in the water? Who's that looking at herself?"

Ti Jeanne got scared, because she heard the voice but couldn't see who it belonged to. Not daring to move, she asked in a feeble voice:

"Who you talkin but not showin youself?"

A throaty chuckle came from the dark, then a rustle. Ti Jeanne saw circular ripples on the water emerging from under the foliage, and then the face of an old old African woman emerged from the water. She had tattoos, and wore large earrings and strands and strands of necklaces made of colourful beads.

"Ti Jeanne, Ti Jeanne," the woman sang in her rusty old voice, "Ti Jeanne, so beautiful, washerwoman, blanchisseuse! Ti Jeanne, mmh, mmh."

As her song changed to a humming sound, rising and falling, the old woman rose and rose, and Ti Jeanne, who was by now totally entranced in spite of her fear, saw that the hag had the body of an anaconda.

"Maman Dlo," Ti Jeanne whispered. "Maman Dlo, I didn't mean to be rude. I didn't hurt anything." For the girl knew that punishment awaits the one who offends the forest creatures, the plants or the animals, and she was in great fear to be talked to by the great water spirit.

"Vanity, vanity, my child," said Maman Dlo, who was now fully seven feet erect on her snakebody, swaying from side to side. "Looking at yourself in the water's reflection. But beautiful you are, ssssssso beautiful! Mmh, mmh!"

Ti Jeanne, entranced, started to swing along with Maman Dlo. As she listened to her song, the girl got up from her seat, and slowly walked into the water. Maman Dlo's tail flapped furiously, creating bigger and bigger splashes, waves, and foam started to rise. Ti Jeanne's chemise fell from her, her hair grew long, covering her round shoulders and her bare breasts, and when the girl's lips reached the water's surface, the bubbles covered the pool as if hundreds of laundresses had been working.

Maman Dlo had enchanted Ti Jeanne, who was to live with her and serve her forever after. She gave the girl a fishtail, and Ti Jeanne was to become one of the most beautiful of the fairy maids, playing with the other river spirits and protecting the forest, its waters and pools for a long time to come.

When the villagers came to look for her, they found only the laundry she had washed, and next to it on the riverbank the chemise she had been wearing and seven shiny fishscales.

Ti Jeanne in later times also chose a husband from amongst the village folk, but that is another story and shall be told another time.

"MAMA DLO" OR "MAMA GLO", whose name is derived from the French "maman de l' eau", which means "mother of the water", is one of the lesser-known personalities of Trinidad and Tobago folklore.

A hideous creature, her lower half takes the form of an anaconda. She is sometimes thought to be the lover of Papa Bois, and old hunters tell stories of coming upon them in the "High Woods". They also tell of hearing a loud, cracking sound, which is said to be the noise made by her tail as she snaps it on the surface of a mountain pool or a still lagoon.

Mortal men who commit crimes against the forest, like burning down trees or indiscriminately putting animals to death or fouling the rivers, could find themselves married to her for life, both this one and the one to follow.

Sometimes she takes the form of a beautiful woman singing silent songs on still afternoons, sitting at the water's edge in the sunlight, lingering for a golden moment, a flash of green-gone. If you meet Mama Dlo in the forest and wish to escape her, take off your left shoe, turn it upside down and immediately leave the scene, walking backwards until you reach home.

Mama Dlo's Gift

FROM THE TIME OF HER EARLIEST MEMORIES, she always entered the forest quietly, silently stepping, slowly moving through the dew-wet underbrush, trying not to tread too hard.

She paused, not so much to listen but to learn, to learn the feel of the day, for every day was different in her forest. Her forest—it lay along a steep valley through which rushed a river called "Shark", halting only in selected places to make pools deep and sure with eddies that swirled backwards in their own placid repose, slick on the surface, secret in their tumultuous depths, where enormous, ancient trees stood sentinel. All fast asleep in ageless repose, same height, same girth, same breadth as though created simultaneously by some mighty hand that reached out from eternity and sowed their dreams in unison so long ago, before words like day or night were made to punctuate the passage of time.

Time had been invented by one of her ancestors, she was sure. Before she entered her forest, she left it, together with her shoes, down by the road. Papita had told her about the Caribs of long ago, their family, the old people who owned all the land. She had told her about the river and of the Oriyu, the water spirits. She always felt that she had just missed them and that, had she come a little earlier, she would have seen them. But she was always just in time to see the ripples they left on the water fade away into placidity. Sometimes, she heard a loud slap upon the surface of the pool. Once, she saw an enormous shape turn around and around in the water like a wheel. Today, she saw the face. A shimmer just beneath the surface of the pool, it seemed to call out with open mouth. A song, she thought. Now she knew for certain that there was a Maman Dlo living in Shark River.

After that, she would bring flowers and pretty buttons, a buckle from a shoe, a dolly's head, quite pink, with staring eyes of blue and tiny holes where hair would have been implanted. She brought little gems made of red and green glass, pins and pretty bow clips. One morning, as she slipped in silence through the woods, the river, coursing with a roar through the rocks and bolders, gray and striped with white lines, she saw something glimmer in the water. It was a lovely comb made of shell and silver, gold-tipped. She stood there entranced, the river foam, a lacy frock around her legs. She picked up the comb and ran it through her hair. At once, she heard music, a song, sighing, which filled her heart with yearning—for what? She had no idea. She knew she must keep this gift a secret.

She would spend her days sitting in the sunshine where the water fell from high up to crash upon the rocks, its spray a brilliant rainbow iridescent about her, combing her long, black hair and listening to Maman Dlo's comb. She learnt that Amana was her true name and that she had a sister who was called Yara, "beautiful river", which flew into a bay not too far away. Others were called Marianne, Madamas and Paria. She heard the sirens' song of sailors who had been dashed to death upon the rocks at Saut d'Eau, and learned not to dread the deafening silence of the forest.

She saw the stranger come into her forest. He grew afraid at her sight, his eyes were startled. She did not smile but combed her hair, listening to the melody of Maman Dlo's song. The river's spray made iridescent colours swirl about her. He ran away. They laughed at him. He would return.

In the time that followed, whenever she combed her hair with the magic comb, she heard a voice that warned her of her curiosity for the stranger and cautioned her to dismiss him from her memory. Maman Dlo's voice came to her like a mother's plea to remain pure and not fall victim to curiosity. But she longed to meet the stranger and would dream him with her in the river.

One day, Maman Dlo rose up from the water to tell her "no". She saw her terrible beauty, her feminine form conjoint with that of a massive anaconda that swirled about and slapped the water with its tail, making a sound like the cracking of huge branches. "No," Maman Dlo breathed, "don't go." But go she did and as time went by, her comb no longer sang its silent song. Mr. Borde and herself would build a house at Cachepa Point and live a happy life.

Close upon a century later, as a very old woman, she sat to the back of a pirogue which was plunging through a turbulent sea towards Yara bay in the hope of beaching at the river's mouth. The outboard engine wined and coughed, and the huge waves threatened to swamp the overcrowded boat. She sensed the terror in the group and took an old, broken comb with an unusual shape out of her pocket. Standing up in the plunging boat and steadying herself, she called to the tillerman to point the bow at the river's mouth and asked the passengers to pray. In a voice at first old and frail, then strong and commanding, she began to sing:

"Maman Dlo, oh Maman Dlo, save us from this terror sea. Be calm, be calm," she told the waves, "Be slow, lie low."

The swirling waters seemed to pause and flatten into an insulent roll that fell away at her call.

"Ma Dolly calmed the sea," they would later say. "She calmed the sea at Yara Bay."

Jumbies and Duennes

<hr/>

THINKING ABOUT DEATH, he slipped away from Lapeyrouse cemetery through the Tragarete Road gate and began to make his way home. He knew that they would miss him, even see him go—he didn't know. What he did know, however, was that he did not want to stay through to the end and hear the thud of the earth falling on the mattress they always put on the coffin to cushion the sound.

Robbie had been his friend from the time they were about three. He had lived right across the street. They had seen each other every day ever since. It had come as a surprise to realise that his partner, his buddy, was gone. For eleven years they had gone to school together, fought in the road, both been in love with Janice Lockhart, shared food from the same plate, slept in the same bed, "brothers of the spear" all the way. Now this boy just gone and dead—wow.

In the fading evening light he walked up Stanmore Avenue. The streets seemed empty and bathed in a pale gray glow. It would be good if he could make it to the tram stop opposite Marli Street. Then he could ride the Savannah car all the way home, or nearly.

As it turned out, he missed the car, and decided to walk through the Savannah. The night came on quickly. The setting sun blended with the rising moon, which appeared fully mature, accompanied by an icy wind and the smell of wreaths and newly-turned earth.

The wide stretch of the Queen's Park Savannah lay before him. He was from around here, so he knew that many cows grazed in the park. He knew too to avoid the cemetery and how to jump the racetrack railings. He was at home.

He remembered how he and Robbie used to break *l'ecole biche* (skipping school) in the Savannah, spending the whole day up in a big tree, eating *hale filé* (haul string, a toffee) and *cowature pocham* (couverture pot de chambre, a ginger biscuit). He remembered the kite-flying days, kicking ball, turning out in white flannels to bat for St. Francis and blaze Robbie's bowling. Robbie went to Mr. de Four's school. He could remember everything, everything.

They had a whistle, their own code to call each other. If you put words to it, it would go "Monkeeeee eric! Monkeeeee eric!" He whistled it now, loudly, over and over, as loud as he could, then again even louder, to the echo this time. That startled him—he looked around the clear, lit ground, almost expecting—what? Ahead, on the Circular Road, the tram that he had missed passed with a clang. It passed the big silk cotton tree, the café and the Overseas Forces' Club. At the corner of Cadiz Road, it stopped to let off a flock of pretty girls in big hats, lacy dresses and white stockings. He vaulted the Savannah rail, sprinted across the street and headed for Industry Lane, where he lived with his granny, never noticing the little fellow who had appeared with the echo, and who now hovered just a little off the ground with knees slightly bent and feet facing the direction from which he had come.

He didn't know why, but after that evening he often walked through the Savannah from Marli Street to Cadiz Road. Many a night he used to whistle, "Monkeeee eric!"—loud, until the sound of his whistling would come back as an echo which never failed to startle him a little. Then, with queasy sort of fear, a slight panic, he would run, vault the Savannah rail, and head for Industry Lane and home. The little fellow would fly unseen behind him, taking with him a whiff of old flowers and stagnant water.

In the morning, he would wake up to the smell of the smoke from the coal-pot, blending with the rich aroma of chocolate boiling. He and his grandmother lived in a little two-bedroom house on a small plot of land under the shade of a very large breadfruit tree. As an only child, he was accustomed to be by himself and, although he really missed his partner Robbie, he was busy attending Mr. Pantin's school for Pitman's shorthand and bookkeeping. He liked to go to the cinema, Olympic, Royal or Rialto, to the 4.30 matinee.

One afternoon in the Royal, alone in "house", watching The Hunchback of Notre Dame for the second time, he heard the whistle. It made him jump. It seemed to come from very close, almost in his ear. He looked around the darkened space—no one, except quite up in the back, two people kissing. The huge beam of the projector was slicing through the dark.

Rain was drizzling as he left the Royal that night. Not a cat in the road as he walked quickly up Charlotte Street. As he crossed Oxford Street, he looked back. He thought he saw a strange reflection in the wet and shiny street. Just beyond the streetlight a white shape flashed on the ground. He quickened his step. He knew the town had strange things aplenty, but he was not in that. As he turned into the lane, almost at his gate, he heard the whistle, low, from far off. He ducked inside and went to bed.

That night he dreamt that he and Robbie were playing "bloké", standing side by side, pitching marbles into a hole in the wall behind his grandmother's kitchen. Robbie had hundreds of bright, glassy marbles. All he had were some dull gray "codens" and two blue "quiawoue". He turned in his bed and halfway woke up and thought he was dreaming that he was hugging a little, naked baby with icy cold feet.

The next morning he woke up late and there was a funny smell like pee. He spent the day alone; his grandmother had gone by train to San Fernando and would come back about midday the following day. That afternoon he went for a walk on the pitch round the Savannah. He sat in the Botanical Gardens, looking at the children playing, and he whistled his habitual whistle, "Monkeeeeee eric!" Later he took his tea in the little gallery, enjoying the haunting zither music that was the theme of a radio programme about a man called Harry Lyon, who had been shot in Vienna. That's when he heard the whistle. It sounded like it came from inside. As he rose to look, he saw the little fellow hovering just inside the gate. A fat little baby with his feet turned backwards and a wide old-time straw hat on his head. His whole body went cold. He knew it was a duenn.

Quickly the vision faded. That night he stayed up until Rediffusion went off the air with a prayer at eleven o'clock. He kept all the lights on in the house and sat in the tiny drawing room until sleep overtook him in the wee hours. Sure enough, he dreamt of the little fellow floating around, whistling "Monkee eric".

The next morning he couldn't stay alone. He took a tram down to the railway station to wait for his grandmother. Because he knew old Mr. Popplewell, the ticket collector, he was allowed to wait on the platform for the train. With a rush, much hissing and great clanging, the big old train filled up the station. There was his granny, nice and plump and real, with a bag of paw-paw balls for him and lots of news from Auntie Leone. That afternoon he told her about the duenn. She became quite still and looked long and hard at him.

"He was your friend. You called him back," she said. "You know Robbie came from China when he was little. He came to the Lees, he was their sister's son. I don't think they baptised him."

It occurred to him that the one thing he and Robbie had not done together was First Communion. That very afternoon his grandmother set to work. She swept the house and yard with a new cocoyea broom. She turned his bed around so he now slept with his head to the west. That night she prayed, "Out of the depths we cry to you...", and as he went to bed she sprinkled holy water, which she always kept in a little bottle in the cabinet, around his bed. Then, she sat in the rocker at his side to wait, her chaplet in hand.

He stayed up as long as he could, but the orange peel tea she had given him eventually took effect and he drifted off to sleep. She was just dozing when the cocks in the breadfruit tree started to crow. Their noise woke her, but what brought her to her senses was the little fellow who hovered just inside the door. "Monkeee eric," he whistled softly, "monkee eric!" Making the sign of the cross, she got up and went to him.

"He can't play with you again, Robbie, you have to go back now where you come from." She raised the little bottle with the holy water, letting some drops fall.

"I baptise you in the name of the Father, the Son and the Holy Ghost, Amen. Go home now, Robbie, go home."

To prevent similar experiences with duennes, never call your children's names out loud in the open, as a duenn might overhear and lure them away. Also, you shouldn't whistle in the middle of the Savannah, or whistle in the dark night. Robbie might be looking for a tree to climb...

The Jumbie of the
Big Silk Cotton Tree

LOOK AT THAT CLOCK! IT'S TIME I'M OFF." Lastique is riding down the road, his bicycle only swerving ever so slightly. Squeak, squeak goes the chain—must have been years ago that it saw a drop of oil.

Cap shoved back to his neck, Lastique is whistling to himself, his bony knees sticking out as he pushes the pedals. He has had a good day and a better evening - Glen Miller is so sweet! And life is sweet too since Camp Ogden offered employment to Lastique: what could be nicer than working on the Yankees' cars in the yard with Radio WVDI playing music for all who have ears to hear?

Friday is payday, and Lastique's pocket rings clink-clink with the coins as his legs go up and down pedalling his bike. Down Long Circular Road, past the newly opened Country Club—"that Canning fellow is real cunning!"—and into Boissière Village—"I wonder if old Miss Ellinore is still around". Ah, the Savannah breeze, how it hits you when you're a bit hot from riding so hard—or is it from the little grog you had with your friends after work?

Lastique slows down a bit. All of a sudden, he feels tired, and Erthig Road seems far. Must be the week of hard work backlashing! Those Yankees don't fool around when it comes to work: six o'clock sharp in the morning, and on and on all day. Thank God for the Misses Chin—they always keep something good in the pot for him when he comes home. It's really not so easy for a man alone—and since Bernice died, he wouldn't know what he would have done without the Misses Chin, such good neighbours!

With the bicycling, the evening's rum is wearing off, and Lastique feels his stomach growling. Passing the St. Ann's turnoff, it's downhill from here, and he lets go of the handlebars to cruise.

What was that? That sound? Sounded like a baby crying from under the big silk cotton tree.

Lastique grabs the handlebar, pushes back his left foot, brakes. Just at the corner cafe—it's closed now—he turns around. Yes, it's a baby crying from under the big silk cotton tree. He peers hard into the darkness from where the whining is coming. Then he leans his bike against the curb and slowly approaches the large roots of the tree. My word! There it is!

A tiny baby, wrapped in a gray shawl. But how did it get here? Whose baby is it? Lastique picks it up, looks around. "Where is your mummy, little chunks?"

Nobody is in sight. Carrying the baby a bit awkwardly in his arms, Lastique circles the tree—nobody. He looks up and down the Savannah—nobody. Belmont Circular Road—empty. Everybody has gone to sleep—it's really late, old man. Hopefully the Misses Chin have left a plate of food for me on the porch! The baby has stopped crying now and looks up at Lastique, tears still moist in its big, round eyes.

"Well, I'm going to take you to the hospital. Maybe somebody knows you there?"

Mounting his bike with some difficulty, balancing the baby in his left arm, Lastique pushes himself off the curb and starts going down the road. But what is this! This baby seems to get heavier and heavier! It's real heavy now, you know! Passing the convent, the child says suddenly in a man's voice:

"You'd better take me back where you found me."

Goodheavensjesusmariaandjoseph! Lastique almost drops it in terror. What ghost is this? Horrified, he turns around on the empty street and pedals, as fast as his stick-out knees take him, back to the silk cotton tree. Sweat is now pouring down his face and he looses his cap but doesn't even notice it. As he draws nearer the tree, the baby shrinks steadily back to its original weight and is deposited, once more a bawling baby, at the foot of the giant tree.

It's all Lastique can do now not to throw it back among the huge roots! He jumps off the bike, the bike falls half in the road, two, three, four big steps and he places the bundle like a hot potato in that same corner. Turn around! Back on the bike! Off we go!

Was it his imagination? Or did it really talk like a man? What a confusion! It looked like a baby, so what's going on?

"Better not meddle with that," mumbles Lastique to himself as he flies down the Savannah, into Hermitage Road. His heart pounding, he rushes into his house, almost knocking over the plate of food that the Misses Chin left for him on the little wall surrounding the porch. He grabs it, and once inside, he locks the door good, and sits down on his only chair in the drawing-room. The plate in his hand is shaking badly. Lastique now notices that he has lost his cap.

The moon, a silent witness, hides his face in a cloud as a chill wind blows and an owl flies out of the great silk cotton tree.

Duendes' Mead

When the sun has sunk to rest,
Somewhere—who knows—in the west,
O'er yon fairy dome that marks the crest
Of the towering Spanish Main;
And skies erewhile in crimson drest
Doff their mangle, and in plain
Hodden-gray are clad again;
When the darkness 'gins to thicken,
(Ah, that hour of doom,
Then it is sweet babes do sicken,
To their early tomb),
And lifeless things beseem to quicken
'Mid the growing gloom;
See, along the shelving strand,
Over shingle, over sand,
Over cruel rocks, unmeet
For little toddling feet,
One by one, or hand in hand
Tiny figures steal along
In a shadowy band.
Without father, without mother,
Without God to bless,
Close they cling
To one another
In their helplessness.

(from *Legends of the Bocas*, A.D. Russell, 1922)

"Duennes" are spirits of children who died before they were baptised. They are fated to roam the forests of Trinidad, practising their wide repertoire of pranks, mostly on living children who are enticed away into the forest and then left abandoned. Duennes are sexless, their feet are turned backwards and they have no faces (although they do have small round mouths). On their rather large heads they wear huge mushroom-shaped straw hats.

To prevent the duennes from calling your children into the forest at dusk, never shout their names in open places, as the duennes will take their names, call them and lure them away.

Legends of Tobago

CARTON OTTLEY REMEMBERS harvest time in Tobago. He describes how after the last load of canes had been ground and the last hogsheads (barrels) of sugar were rolled into the curing house, the fires under the boilers were put out and the preparations for crop over began.

The estate owner as a rule contributed a young bull for the festivities. Heaps of ground provisions, chickens, suckling pigs and other foodstuffs were brought in by the "metayers" and several demijohns of good alcoholic beverage, distilled right there on the estate, were much in evidence.

On crop over night, the metayers and their family and friends gathered in the millyard. The wings of the huge windmill were silhouetted against the darkening sky, creaking softly. Large pots of food had been cooking all day. Fiddlers found their bows and tightened up the strings, tuning their instruments. The goat skin men, the drummers, warmed their drums over a coconut branch fire, tapping them from time to time to hear if the right pitch was achieved.

Old Clay picked up a beat, and Balmoral de Noon followed quickly on his fiddle. Old Bacchus' grandson was the steel man, tinkling away. Thus the music started, fiddlers and drummers giving their best. With the music, the dance began. Men and women went round

the blazing fire, dancing quadrilles, reels, jigs and polkas—dances which had supplanted the dances of their ancestors, but with the tempo that remained true over the ages.

Later, when everybody had eaten their fill and danced to drop, and the blazing fire had begun to burn low, men would sing the songs of long ago, tunes of African origin, and songs that they made up themselves.

In those days, they took about a week off during crop over. It was a time to recover from the work of the harvest, but also from the revelries themselves!

At that time, there still lingered in Tobago that long twilight that had begun well before the end of the 19th century, even before Tobago and Trinidad had been joined into one crown colony. Tobago had gone into an economic slumber.

The busy little island of 100 to 150 years before, that had enriched cotton planters from England and made fortunes for Dutch bankers, was now almost a wasteland. Sugarcane production had stopped as a result of the collapse of the merchant trading house of Gillespie in London, which folded after the fall of the price of sugar. The great windmills of the southern flatlands at Lowlands and Bacolet were now still. The waterwheels that had turned the mills in the lush valleys spun aimlessly. The great houses, unpainted, neglected, some abandoned, were being sold off.

Since emancipation, Tobagonians had created a strong village life, extending family and kinship under the aegis of Moravian preachers and later Methodist pastors. The school system produced individuals of particular academic merit, some outstanding.

As the estates were sold off, they were acquired increasingly by the Tobagonians themselves. Out of this shift in landholding arose a sensitivity to property and ancestral land. The heritage of the older heads was embedded in the Tobagonian collective consciousness. At the time of Ottley's writing, one could say that virtually every Tobago family owned land and possessed a house.

In this period, there was calm for some, economic depression for others. In the long quiet evenings, the sparks from the coalpot snapping in the wind, the stories of long ago were told. The children drew near, the "Home Sweet Home" etchings on the glass chimneys of the pitch-oil lamps throwing huge wavering shadows on the walls. The storytellers would recount the powers of men of old, of an old slave woman who had the gift of stopping a windmill at a glance, and the one who was able to cause the master's wife's back to raise in welts whenever one of her own was abused. There were stories of fairy maids who lived beneath the wheel at Arnos Vale and took the nice-looking boy from Culloden for three days—some people say because he had smooth, glowing skin. Upon his return, he had wisdom where before he had been simple. He grew wealthy, buying one, then another, sugar estate. His son died, however, drowning...

The Legend of Gang Gang Sara

THE LEGEND OF GANG GANG SARA, the African witch of Golden Lane, has its origins in the latter half of the 18th century.

On a stormy night she was blown from her home in Africa across the sea to Tobago and landed quite safely at the village of Les Coteaux. From there, she journeyed to Golden Lane in search of her family, who had long ago been transported there. She lived to a great age and is remembered for her wisdom and kindness.

She became the loving wife of Tom, whom legend says she had known as a child in her native Africa. After her Tom died, wishing to return to her native land, she climbed a great silk cotton tree and tried to fly, not knowing that she had lost the art of flight as a result of having eaten salt.

To this day the names of Tom and Sara can be seen inscribed upon the headstones of their graves, where they have lain side by side for close upon two hundred years.

Mermaids and Fairymaids

THERE BE MERMAIDS HERE AND LEVIATHANS, great denizens of the deep. Among the swirling currents and white-capped blue-green waters, just where the Caribbean Sea meets the Atlantic Ocean, close by St. Giles and near to Misty Marble Island, past Anse Gouleme and Anse Brisant, towards Bird of Paradise Island and down the coast past Speyside to Fat Hog Bay, it is remembered from long ago that this was where the mermaids came to play.

Tobago mermaids are male and live in the deep, deep sea. They mate with the fairy maids of the rivers and the secret mountain pools. Riding upon the crests of waves, they are handsome men like kings of old or warriors of long ago, beplumed and richly garbed. They may grant a wish, transform mediocrity into genius, and confer wealth and power.

Sometimes the water people seek relationships with mortals. Some men are particularly attractive to the fairymaids, especially men with smooth skin.

The fairymaid is said to be beautiful with long lush hair and one tiny foot in the shape of a deer's hoof. She may use her power to "turn" a man's head. She may steal his shadow and leave him quite demented. In which case, accompanied by friends and family and with the help of a "workman", he must go to the river and address the water, pleading for the restoration of his lost shadow. This done, he must leave the water's edge and not look back.

Fairymaids may be found in caves behind waterfalls or beneath certain bridges where the river runs deep and swift. In days gone by, they were seen near certain waterwheels.

To discontinue a relationship with a fairy queen, an offering of two pairs of shoes must be made. The first must be burnt on the beach. The fairymaid will then rise out of the water and ask if she is to be paid for past services. The answer must be, "nothing but this pair of shoes". The second pair must then be thrown into the waves.

Town and Country Customs

L APEYROUSE CEMETERY IN PORT OF SPAIN is one of the best illustrations of this country's cosmopolitan population. It contains the graves and tombs of the rich and the poor. Reading the inscriptions is a veritable "tour de force" of the known world.

There are rows of graves with Chinese inscriptions, as well as small mansions for the French aristocratic dead. Elegant monuments commemorate the more conservative British, and imposing rotundas and tall obelisks mark eminent freemasons of a previous century.

The various religious rites performed at Lapeyrouse are a true reflection of the country's multi-faceted society. On a busy afternoon, one can hear the clapping and chanting of the Shouters, while from not too far away comes the murmur of the Catholics working at their beads. In the gathering dusk, the mournful tubas of the Salvation Army Band keep pace with alarming flats and sharps as rendered by the reeds and woodwinds. You can hear a kaiso or two and sometimes very good pan. The smell of flowers is often mingled with that of exotic incense, and at times there is the bang and flash of firecrackers. This is for the Chinese.

Indeed, the origins of Lapeyrouse are closely connected to the establishment of present-day Trinidad. Pico de la Peyrouse, a French nobleman, came to Trinidad in 1778. He was a friend and companion of Philip Rose Roume de St. Laurent. His older brother was one of those intrepid explorers who circumnavigated the globe towards the end of the 18th century.

Pico acquired land on the outskirts of Port of Spain, a muddy little village in those days, and together with a gang of slaves he cleared the dense forest and laid out the first sugarcane estate on the island. Pico also built the first factory there for the production of Muscovado sugar, brown, wet and smelling of molasses. He may have been our first exporter. The Otaheite variety of sugarcane did well and so did the de la Peyrouse family.

No one knows quite where the burial ground was before the Lapeyrouse cemetery was established. It had served a small village,

now lost in the suburbs of Port of Spain, bordering on the estate or perhaps in it. It was called "Campo Santo" (the holy field). The earliest grave is said to have been one for Jean Creteau, who died in 1745.

Port of Spain grew and prospered, and by the time of the British conquest in 1797 it was in need of a bigger and better burial ground. This was marked off in a small area bordered by Tragarete Road, Richmond Street and Fraser Street. A wall was erected around it, and by 1813 it was referred to as the "Old Cemetery".

The records concerning the purchase of land from the de la Peyrouse family by the Cabildo have long since been destroyed by the various fires that have swept the town over the years. It would appear, however, that the Littlepage family business did tender for the erection of a wall around the "New Cemetery". This new burial ground acquired the name "Lapeyrouse" by 1831, being on the old estate lands.

By 1823, colonial order was being generally imposed on this unruly, very heterogeneous and bacchanal-prone island. This was highlighted by the inauguration of a section of Lapeyrouse for Anglicans towards the western wall. Not to be outdone, there was soon a place for Catholics — the eastern side.

Within just a few years, the cemetery was again enlarged, this time by buying lands from the Shine family, who were originally Irish and are related to the Park and Black families. One Herr Schuler, a German, was employed as keeper. It is interesting to note that several remarkable people became keepers of the cemetery in the 19th century: P.G.L. Borde, for example, the notable historian, and also José Numa Dessource, an early socialist reformer who attempted to start a colony in Venezuela.

Over the next few years, more land was acquired by the Cabildo, this time from Joseph Dert (pronounced "Der"), the son of Benoît Dert, who had started Trinidad's first coffee estate in an area between Queen's Park South and Tragarete Road (now part of Newtown) in the 1770s. Benoît also introduced freemasonry to Trinidad through the establishment of Lodge United Brothers, which is still in existence today.

Governor Sir Ralph Woodford, who held office in Trinidad from 1813 to1829, worked hard for the cause of racial segregation in Trinidad, to the extent of marking off a portion of Lapeyrouse cemetery for the free black people of the town. This in fact cost Schuler his job, as for various reasons he lost track of the incoming dead and often buried the blacks among the whites and vice versa. The matter was amended only "as far as circumstances will admit". It must have been extremely upsetting for the white dead who had avoided personal contact with the blacks throughout their entire lifetimes, to find themselves sharing the same worms in death...

In those times, Trinidad possessed chain gangs, prisoners chained together, who were set to work building roads like Lady Chancellor Road, cutting canals like Harts Cut in Chaguaramas (which was filled in during the Second World War), and digging graves. The men in the chain gang were whipped on a regular basis by a slave called Cinq Sous ("five cents"). After Cinq Sous' untimely death, the Illustrious Cabildo was forced to advertise for a new whipper.

Just as today, the cemetery was populated by both the living and the dead, and efforts were constantly made to stop the robbing of tombs of their monuments and mortuary decorations. There was also an active trade in skulls and other bones for the purpose of obeah. Corpses were sometimes exhumed by robbers in search of gold and other valuables and reports were made to the police of the finding of smashed dentures where gold had been removed from them. So much for "R.I.P." — rest in piece.

In the period just before emancipation, that part of town was pretty rough. There was stickfighting and brawling on an ongoing basis. Corbeaux Town's name was well earned. Port of Spain's jamette society staged spectacular funerals that were remembered more than 100 years later by oral tradition. This was recorded by Mitto Sampson in the 1940s, who was otherwise known as "Strong Man". Sampson was famous for his death-defying hangman's leap from the Dry River bridge, a noose being fastened to it and then placed around his neck.

The cemetery grew in direct proportion to the town, eventually covering some 20 acres. By the 1840s, Ariapita estate, which had once belonged to the wife of Roume de St. Laurent, had been developed for housing. So had Tranquillity, acquired from the Cummings family. Newtown, once part of the St. Clair estate, was also opened up. Streets were laid out and people moved in. There was an air of prosperity about the place, which was of course reflected at Lapeyrouse cemetery with magnificent mausoleums, some containing chapels where masses might have be sung in Latin, even then a dead language.

The cholera epidemics of 1854 wrought terrible havoc in the town. The connection between the cesspits and the waterwells in most people's back yards was not made until too late and Lapeyrouse possesses a certain melancholy for the quantity of graves from that time with the names and years of life of the town's very young inhabitants.

Burying people in the tropics had to be done quickly, even hastily. There was the case of an indentured Indian who was to be buried prematurely. Fortunately for him, his cries were heard coming from his coffin by some soldiers of the West India Regiment. He was saved. For many years later, he was known as "Lapeau" (after Lapeyrouse) and made his living as a rat catcher.

Great samaans once lined Main Street in Lapeyrouse. Only two are left. No longer are there royal palms trailing yellow-tail-birds' nests. The famous American naval commander Commodore Perry is remembered on the Tragarete Road side in "Perry Gate". The brass plaques have since been stolen by vandals. On the eastern side, Daniel Hart erected a massive arch in the 1840s as the main entrance to Lapeyrouse, which was once flanked by elaborate cast iron lamps. These have long been stolen and sold. There was once a lovely water fountain — this too has gone.

The tombstones of Lapeyrouse make interesting reading, ranging from the simple to the hilarious. One wag had engraved on his marker: "Fart free, wherever you be, for this was the death of me."

There is also the well-known "Malice to none, charity to all", and this inscription which you can find near to the southern gate:

Stop, traveller, e'er you go by
So are you now, so once was I
As I am now, soon you will be
Prepare yourself to follow me.

The Traditional Wake

THE WAKE FOR A DECEASED member of the village is a noisy affair and almost not at all sad! Several of the activities of a wake are depicted in the picture above: the "raconteur", who is regaling the children with his stories; the limbo dancers who need strong thigh and back muscles to succeed; and, inside the house, the neighbours, family members and friends who came to sing hymns and mourn the deceased. Below are the bongo dancers, challenging each other with their complicated choreographies.

Card playing is going on, and kind women have baked cookies, biscuits and other goodies and pass them around with coffee. A wake usually takes place at night, when flambeaux light the yard, making the shadows of the visitors dance upon the bark of the trees.

Limbo

IS AN ATHLETIC "DANCE GAME" played at wakes. Its origin is lost in time, but West African visitors seem to recognise a slight resemblance to one of their children's games. In any case, this dance is wholly Trinidadian. Like calypso, it is popular throughout the West Indies.

Limbo is the reverse of the high jump. A stick is held by two men at about three feet high and dancers pass under without touching the bar, to the singing of the chantwell, accompanied by the beating of the qua qua (dried bamboo slits). No part of the body except the sole of the feet should touch the ground. As the stick is lowered after each round, the dancers keep falling back to the ground, leaving only the most supple man or woman to claim championship honours.

Bongo

A FOLK-DANCE, THIS COMPLICATED, athletic pastime is usually performed at wakes. It relies on the principle that one dancer has to repeat the movement of the other, plus add one of his own. As the bongo goes on, the movements become more and more intricate, as one dance-step, twist or turn is added on top of the other. The winner is the dancer who can repeat the other's movements to perfection and with beauty, and the loser is the one who fails in remembering the string of movements.

The bongo is usually accompanied by handclapping and "qua-qua"—that is, two pieces of bamboo rhythmically beaten together.

Shango

THIS SYNCRETIC CULT, formed by the descendants of African slaves in the Caribbean from a mixture of African deities and Christian beliefs, has several other names in the New World: Santeria, Voudoun and Candomble. Shango is a Yoruba god, but the name also refers to the cult, as well as to the ceremony and the dance.

Shango tents are places where possessions take place, where sacrifices are made, and where drums are beaten, to whose rhythm the dancers and singers fall into trances.

Shango ceremonies are performed in the rural areas of the Caribbean islands, and are usually open to anyone who wishes to attend, especially to those who have a special wish for their future or a special regret of the past—or just to give thanks.

Cockfighting

"GAYELLE" IS THE NAME FOR the ring in which either cockfighting or stickfighting takes place. In the old days, the gayelle was located in remote areas, far away from the village. The law often prescribed against the bloody pastimes taking place there.

Cockfighting is, in fact, a common practice in rural areas, not only in the Caribbean, but in Latin America and southern Europe as well. It was probably brought to the Caribbean by Spanish and French immigrants, and is to this day very popular in Latin countries.

To own a successful fighting rooster was regarded as an honour and also a good source of income for many men. The stakes of betting on the roosters were often very high, and the fighting birds were trained and fed with special care.

As it is a fight to the death for the animals, cockfighting, like bullfighting, is regarded as cruel by modern society and has been outlawed in many regions.

Stickfighting

"BOIS!" WAS THE CRY accompanying the stickfighters in the "gayelle", meaning "Wood!" The whole affair is loaded with patois words, derived from French: the "baton" is the stick, made of local poui wood, and the "batonnier" is the stickfighter.

Stickfighting was once extremely widespread, and intricately connected to carnival. The early carnival bands had their leading "chantuelles", singers who were also stickfighters, who led the bands and challenged each other to fight either verbally with "kalinda" songs, or with batons.

Today, the Caribbean martial art of stickfighting has been revived in many areas in the countryside. There is usually a little blood involved, as one of the batonniers might sustain a "buss head", but also a lot of fun and rum.

The Bake Shop

THE STAPLE FOOD of longtime Trinidad and Tobago were fried or baked rolls, called "bakes". With or without grated coconut, they were the food of the poor and the not so poor. The women who ran fry shops were gifted with a "sweet hand", and the smell of their delicious bakes drew hungry people to their makeshift bakery.

On an evening or Saturday, their shops became "liming spots" for the neighbourhood, and many a good calypso was composed on their thresholds. News was exchanged, letters delivered, notes posted, and occasionally, an impoverished "whiteman" would call at the back door to buy a couple of bakes for his dinner.

Amerindian Tales

AN AMERINDIAN PRESENCE HAUNTS the origins of calypso in Trinidad. Over the last hundred years or so, this presence has been thickly overlaid by an Afro-French veneer, displacing this strand that forms a rich and significant weave of the fabric that is part and parcel of Trinidad's national festival. The story goes like this.

The Caribs had all but faded away from Trinidad by the 1840s. They had almost been wiped out by the advent of western civilisation and their remnants had retreated to Venezuela.

With the opening up of the cocoa economy from the 1870s to the 1920s, they had faded back into the wilderness of the Northern Range and had drifted into urban life. This is where we pick up a little-known story, which Mitto Sampson in his paper on calypso legends recounts.

Jo Jo was the son of Thunderstone, who was the chantwell of a band called the Congo Jockos that once dominated upper Nelson Street in Port of Spain. He was reputed to have lost his wife Cariso Jane to Surisima the Carib, a well-known calypso singer. Jo Jo, in his 90s, told Mitto in 1947 about Surisima the Carib.

The word cariso, by which term calypso was known prior to the 1890s, is descended from the Carib term "Carieto," meaning a joyous song. Surisima was famous also as a folklorist and raconteur. He would be paid by people to come to their homes and tell stories of long ago. He was a wayside historian in the style of the late José Ramon Fortuné, Clemmy George, Harry Pitts and Alfredo Codallo. Whenever he spoke, people gathered.

Jo Jo possessed the Carib tradition. Carietos, he said, could heal the sick with music, embolden the warrior and seduce the beautiful. It is said that during the reign of the cacique Guamatumane in Spanish times (before 1797), singers of carieto were rewarded with special gifts of land, and, apart from the caciques themselves, they also had the most beautiful ladies.

It is related that during the regime of the cacique Guancangari the two great singers were Dioarima, a tall, good-looking, powerful personality, and Casaripo, an "undersized weakling" who had a voice that was capable of making cowards brave, invigorating the poorly and calming the crazy.

Dioarima had two lovely daughters who were watched over day and night. One dark and windy night, a singer hid in the bushes and proceeded to sing several beautiful and hauntingly soulful songs. The songs had a very upsetting effect on the lovely daughters of Dioarima. The singer returned the following night and once again sang his haunting songs. The two girls slipped out into the night and met the singer in the high forest that surrounded the village in which they lived and went with him to Conquerabia (now Port of Spain). The three lived together for many years "in regal splendour", and Dioarima was never able to get back his daughters.

When the Spaniards came to Trinidad, they heard of these wonderful singers whose voices spurred men to battle even in the face of fearful odds. According to Mitto Sampson, "they used bribery and clever manipulation and finally ambushed the two [singers] through the treachery of the Carib slave-woman Coziria. The singers were subjected to unspeakable tortures, and molten lead was poured down their throats."

After Casaripo and Dioarima had been killed, the power of the Caribs began to fade in Trinidad until they were eventually conquered by the Spanish. Guandori, a famous stickman of the 1860s, was the last descendant of the daughters of Dioarima, the fabled singer. He was a great stickman in the tradition of Tiny Satan, Rocou John and Cutaway Rimboud.

"Surisima himself used to organise a procession of Carib descendants from the city of Port of Spain to the heights of El Chiqueno," relates Mitto Sampson. "Up in the mountains of the Northern Range, they would make a huge figure of the Carib slave-woman Coziria, the betrayer of their ancestors, and burn this giant figure after much feasting, drinking and singing of obscene songs. The song remembered from those times went:

Cazi, cazi, cazi, cazi,
Dende, dende, dende, dariba.

Shiffer Brathwaite told Mitto Sampson that his father said when the people sang this song, they remembered and felt the sorrow experienced by the Caribs for the loss and betrayal of Casaripo and Dioarima.

Hy Arima

BEFORE HE CLIMBED THE MOUNTAIN, he had purified himself by vomiting. And as the vanishing sun dropped swiftly into the ocean, he had taken from the hand of the ancient creature a forked tube and sniffed a grayish powder placed in a wooden dish upon the head of a rough-hewn stone statue, which represented the god. Now, past, present and future were one. The cohiba ceremony was enacted by those who would know the will of the gods.

The rolling mists were really a part of the cloudscape that blanketed the summits of the Northern Range. The brilliance of the full moon appearing in an intermittent manner gave an atmosphere to the scene that suggested phantoms. There may indeed have been some.

As far as he knew, there was no difference between himself and the elements about him: the earth, the moon, the sky from which the mist fell, soft rain to rise like mists again... The huge black stone glistened in the damp. Its engraved pictures told a story that he could read only with his heart. A tale so old that it no longer possessed beginning or end, and like the mists it existed in a perpetual state of becoming.

They say his name was Hy Arima, and that he had come to the top of Aripo to be at one with the navel of the world. No one knows who put the pictureglyphs, rock carvings, on this huge boulder embedded in the flank of Cierro Aripo. There are some similar ones "down the Main" in Venezuela and in Colombia. There is no deciphering of these marks, and it is probably impossible to know how long ago they were made.

The story of the tribal people of these islands can barely be gleaned through the mists of time—even though their history came to a violent end only some three hundred years ago. So thorough was the genocide committed by the Europeans of that time. It has been suggested that the earliest Amerindians crossed over from Asia to North America some 40,000 years ago, to what later became known as the New World. Much of the oceans' water was then locked in the glaciers of the polar caps, and the level of the sea was extremely low.

These paleo-Indians, as they are called by archeologists, slowly traveled the length and breadth of North and South America. Hunters and collectors, they used simple tools of stone and wood. Some 15,000 to 20,000 years were to pass before the stone projectiles were hefted on to wooden spears to more effectively hunt the large land mammals which populated the savannahs of the Americas before the end of the ice age—the spear was born. At kill sites in north-west Venezuela, animal bones have been found which show traces of being cut through, and there are projectile points and other stone implements. The West Indies may not have been inhabited during paleo-Indian times, probably because the earliest Amerindians lacked the skill of boat building.

Trinidad, however, was still attached to the mainland during the final millennium of the ice age, more than 8,000 years ago. The Dragon's Mouth sealed the land bridge that connected the island to the continent. Complete skeletons of ice age animals have been found in Trinidad, but no kill sites have yet been discovered. Archeologists like Dr. Ari Boomert, formerly attached to the University of the West Indies, feel convinced that deep in the southern forest of the island those kill sites are still awaiting discovery.

As the climate of the world changed, the ice melted and the seas rose. Trinidad was cut off from the mainland, and possibly Tobago from Trinidad. A different life now emerged for those who lived on this newly made island. The enormous sloth, together with other huge mammals, was now extinct, and the natives, now described as meso-Indians, altered their life-styles. Arrows replaced spears, as animals were now smaller. Shellfish and crustaceans became the main source of food. This forced a knowledge of the sea and seafood, evidenced by fish bones and shells which can be found in huge middens. Those middens could have been in use for hundreds of years.

Boat building enabled the meso-Indians to explore and settle in the islands of the Caribbean chain. The oldest evidence of a settlement suggest a date of some 7,000 years ago and is located in south-east Trinidad. It has been suggested, however, that the Banwari midden, a shell heap at Oropouche, may well be older. These refuse heaps contain bones of deer, agoutis, wild cats and monkeys, and also caimans, iguanas and birds.

Specialised tools and weapons were now developed for hunting and food processing. Ground stone tools such as mortars and pestles for grinding nuts, well polished bone points for fish spears, and finely ground stone axes for felling trees were used by the meso-Indians.

Life remained unaltered for thousands of years. It was not until approximately 300 B.C. that the Guianas and Trinidad were invaded by people with a far more advanced type of culture—tribal people who possessed the knowledge of land cultivation, of crops such as bitter manioc and sweet potatoes, of making pottery and polishing stone implements, of spinning cotton into thread and weaving it into cloth. These Amerindians were a people with a way of living and a society

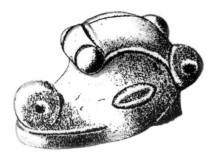

fundamentally different from that of the hunters, fishers and food gatherers of the previous epoch.

They came out of the Orinoco river system, from what would later be called Venezuela and the Guianas, and they are known today as neo-Indians. Archeologists also call them Saladoid people, after a site of that name in eastern Venezuela. The Saladoid people were the first to organise agriculture, villages and long distance travel. They made cassava bread from the manioc root, once the prussic acid had been squeezed out. Baked into large disks, the cassava loaves could be kept for weeks.

It has been guessed that the Saladoid people were the first Arawakan-speaking people in the West Indies. After 300 A.D., another wave of adventurers, the Barrancos, crossed the narrow sea to Trinidad. These were absorbed by the earlier settlers. The difference between them can only be observed in the respective styles of their pottery decoration. These new people migrated to Tobago, and, according to Boomert, influenced the Saladoid peoples of the Lesser Antilles.

Boomert points out that the majority of objects made by the neo-Indians were manufactured of perishable materials, featherwork, basket work and textiles, and as such little idea may be gleaned of their artistic skills. What has survived, however, is pottery or objects made from stone or shell, with the notable exception of a number of finds from the Pitch Lake, such as wooden paddles, war clubs, a bench, a mortar and a bowl.

Some burial sites have been discovered as well, which contain stone axes and pots with remains of food—all this to sustain the deceased on his or her journey to the hereafter.

The legend of Hy Arima is but a whisper in the vast testimony of a now vanished people. Place names around the country echo words from a distant time and serve to maintain a memory of when this land was theirs. We, who have come after, should hold all this in trust, and be awed by the ghostly presence of Trinidad and Tobago's ancient tribal people.

Mausica

MAUSICA ESTATE OFF THE ARIMA OLD ROAD is now no more. The giant immortelles, mother of cocoa, no longer house hundreds of yellow-tail-bird nests. They were cut down years ago to give way to a school and a housing development. The river that ran behind the old estate house has all but disappeared, and the ancient forest from which it sprang has also vanished.

Mausica came into our family more than two hundred years ago when a distant relation of my father's people, who had come from France in the 1780s, married a beautiful half-Spanish, half-Carib girl named Mausica.

It was she who brought with her, as her dowry, her inheritance, the ancient Spanish title to this beautiful piece of Trinidad, and it was after her that the estate was named. This truly beautiful human being, who lived to a great age and was remembered by the older people of Arima up until a generation or so ago, also left behind a wonderful collection of folktales and memories of her mother's people, the Caribs. This is one such tale:

Once upon a time, the Caribs lived on the moon. They didn't call it "moon", but they lived there nevertheless, and the outlines of their land on the moon can be seen by everybody on a cloudless night.

Of course, the Caribs were looking at the earth from their land on the moon, and indeed they were wondering why the earth looked so dark and gloomy. One day they decided to come over and give it a good cleaning, so it would shine brightly. They rode on some clouds, descended to the earth and started to clean it, but when they found they had done enough, they couldn't find their clouds again to return to the moon. They started to pray to their Most Ancient One, but to no avail. As the day grew to a close, they started to be very hungry. On the moon, they would just pick up the nourishing moon dust, mix it with water, form it into pleasant shapes, bake it and eat those moon cakes. They tried to do that with earth's clay, but it grew hard and wasn't edible at all.

The Most Ancient One, however, sent them some birds — which the Caribs had never seen before — which showed them how to pick berries and fruit and eat those. So the Caribs also started to eat fruit and berries, which quelled their first hunger.

After a while, however, they grew tired of the berries. They again prayed to the Most Ancient One, and again their faith was rewarded. In the forest, they found a most miraculous tree, whose branches bore different fruit, and from whose roots sprang all kinds of vegetables: plaintains, cassava, corn and yam.

The Caribs were amazed at the tree, but since they were only used to moondust, again they did not know that this was food. A wild animal came to their help again: this time a wild hog or quenk, which showed them how to rummage in the soft earth and dig out the roots and provisions. The famished Caribs washed all the provisions, put them in the unpalatable clay vessels that they had made and cooked them. What a delicious innovation!

It seemed to become clear that they would not ever be able to return to the moon. When they saw that the fruit and provisions from the miraculous tree were diminishing, again they started to worry about the future. But the Most Ancient One again helped them out: in their sleep, he whispered to them to cut branches from the tree and plant them, so that they in turn would grow to become fruit-bearing. He also told them to keep grains of maize and how to plant some of the roots so they would grow into new plants.

The Caribs did as they were told, and soon their settlement on earth was a beautiful little village, where everybody grew their food around their ajoupas. And they stayed on earth for a long, long time.

Every now and then, they would look up at the moon on a cloudless night, and think of the times when their ancestors ate moondust and in turn looked at the dark earth. And then they would sit down and tell this story to their sons and daughters.

Warahoons' Return

THE PLACID GULF OF PARIA appeared to possess no horizon as the sky and the sea were both a seamless light shade of blue. The canoes—strictly speaking, the corials—seemed to appear quite suddenly from the morning air. Three of them, one quite large, fifty feet or more in length and ten or twelve wide, the keel crafted from a giant tree, the sides built of boards and held together by the seats. Silent as a breeze they sliced the still water, the paddlers making no sound in their endeavour, as they took their craft into the mangrove forest that framed the stone embankment and shipway.

The Roman Catholic Church at Moruga has a sense of grandeur well beyond the rural character of the town. Morning mass had just ended and the congregation, made up of planters from the nearby coconut estates and their slightly overdecorated wives, were mingling in a jovial style with the local shopkeepers and more self-possessed pleasantry, when quite suddenly a large group of completely naked Warahoon Indians were passing, moving through their midst quietly, purposefully, almost as if they were really not there at all. And, in a sense, certainly in the context of their reality, those well-dressed, sweetly scented folks may not have truly existed at all.

For time out of mind, the Indians had travelled annually out of the primeval forest and grasslands of what we call Venezuela and the swamplands of the Orinoco delta to this island. Streaming through the shocked, amused and startled congregation, they crossed the main street, skirted the small common playing field, and headed into the wooded countryside, following an invisible course that took them through people's yards, across cocoa estates and country roads. Handsome, well-formed

90

men, old women, pretty girls, some with babies at their breast, boys running—all they wore was a sort of belt around their waist. Their hair was black and straight, their features were sharp-cut, fair and slightly Asiatic-looking, their limbs were well-rounded, strong and healthy. They carried hammocks, parrots, goats, pigs, bows, very long arrows, stylishly tipped. The Warahoons would trade these things for tobacco or glass beads, mirrors, axes, fishhooks and three-inch nails.

Centuries ago, they had faded from this island, appalled at the depredations of the Spaniards and the unceasing attempts of the priests to dissuade them from their nakedness, their free love and their devotion to the wind, the water, the earth and the flame that was born from the crack of thunder and the bolts of lightning. They had thunderstones which they had kept for hundreds of years.

They had returned to this island, their ancient home, year after year, century after century. They came ashore at Erin, Moruga or Icacos, following the same paths as their people always had. Heading towards where San Fernando is now, they were passing naked through the busy streets and pausing for a while on holy Naparima Hill in memory of long lost times. Then they moved on to the holiest hill of all, Mount Tamana, a flat-topped mesa in the centre of the island, covered in gigantic trees.

They did this in commemoration of their ancient myth of genesis. The great god Jacahuna was displeased, created a great devastation and all the people perished. Two, a man and a woman, had made their escape to the lonely mountaintop of Mount Tamana and survived. The two were able to create anew a human race from the fruits of the Mauritius palm.

For a long, timeless period, the Warahoons stayed and played like children of the forest, maintaining the memory of an antique origin when the world was newly made and few things possessed names. After a while, they retraced their steps back to their corials and quietly slipped away into the golden sunset.

The End of this Book.

The Beginning of New Legends.

Picture sources:

Paria Publishing Company Limited wishes to thank Angostura Limited and Hand Arnold Limited for the kind permission to use the illustrations by Alfred Codallo, which the artist did for these companies in the 1950s as part of their advertising campaigns in the Trinidad Guardian.

The other illustrators were Avril Turner, Stuart Hahn, Sue Anne Gomes and Peter Shim, who produced most of the illustrations of this book.

The engravings of the Amerindians on page 82 was taken from Bryan Edwards' book *Survey of His Majesty's Dominions in the West Indies*, 1793. The illustration of the bathing beauty on page 48 originates from a print in the Tom Cambridge Collection. Both illustrations were engravings done after Augustino Brunias.

Bibliography:

- *Selected works of Alfredo Antonio Codallo* by Holly Gayadeen B.F.A., Dip.Ed.,
  by the author, 1983
- *Voodoo Gods* by Maya Deren
- *Survey of His Majesty's Dominions in the West Indies* by Bryan Edwards, 1793
- *The Folklore of Trinidad* by Harry Pitts, unpublished manuscript
- *Legends of the Bocas* by Alexander David Russell, Cecil Palmer, London 1922
- *Ti-Jean and his Brothers* by Derek Walcott (Paria Publishing)
- *Mermaids and Fairy Maids or Water Gods and Goddesses of Tobago* by H.B. Meikle,
  (Caribbean Quarterly in 1957)
- papers by Ari Boomert and Dr. Phillip Sherlock of the University of the West Indies
- *Folklore and Legends* and *Tales of the Paria Main Road*, collected by Gerard A Besson
  (Paria Publishing)
- *Stories of Mitto Sampson* by Andrew Pearse, in Caribbean Quarterly, 1957
- *Scientific Sorties* by Fr. Anthony de Verteuil
- *Tobago* by Carton Ottley
- *Obeah—Witchcraft in the West Indies* by Hersketh Bell, published first in 1889